FAST GRAMMAR
High School Training
LEVEL 2

Melanie Wilson, Ph.D.

ISBN: 978-1-7354939-7-8

Table of Contents

TOP SECRET

As an advanced recruit into the Fast Grammar program, you have access to this classified information. Please be aware that these training materials are for your eyes only.

As in Level 1 training, you will be part of an elite team of autocorrectors. Behind the scenes, without a user's awareness, you will be correcting mistakes. To serve in this critical role, you will have to master grammar so your corrections can be made in real time.

This Level 2 training regimen is for high school students who have learned basic grammar concepts and are ready to learn how to correct trickier errors. To add to the challenge, you'll be working with two new clients. Again, you should continue your literature and composition studies while working on Fast Grammar missions.

The four missions per operation are structured as they were in Level 1. They may be completed in one session or on four separate weekdays to reinforce the learning. Completing 1 of the 32 operations or 4 unit tests per week will contribute to an English credit for an academic school year (36 weeks).

Each operation begins with a Fast Facts section. Review the section and write examples or complete the exercises as indicated. You'll either review given examples on the next page or will find the solutions at the end of this training manual. Then you'll be ready to work with your clients in simulations being used to prepare you for real-time autocorrection.

- **In your first mission**, you will receive a text update from your client. Knowledge of your clients' intentions will allow you to make accurate corrections.

- **In the second mission**, you will receive a graphic to help you remember the difference between commonly confused words.

- **In the third mission**, you'll be asked to use what you've learned up to that point in your training to review the client's writing. Sometimes your review is structured like a college entrance exam.

- **In the fourth mission**, we'll ask you to correspond with your client and practice what you've learned.

While you're in training, you'll use a digital or physical highlighter to make corrections. The solutions to your missions are at the end of this manual. If you make mistakes, reread the Fast Facts section for that operation. At the end of each unit, your trainer will administer a test to assess your progress. (Tests & solutions are available as a free download at FunToLearnBooks.com/FastGrammar2).

> Find extra practice exercises at FunToLearnBooks.com/ FastGrammar2

At any point in your training, you can find more practice exercises at FunToLearnBooks.com/FastGrammar2. We also recommend applying what you're learning in each operation to your outside literature and writing assignments.

With your commitment to this training program, I am confident you will succeed and will soon join our ranks as a Fast Grammar autocorrector. Please don't hesitate to contact me if you need assistance in your training.

Kirk English

Training Director
info@FunToLearnBooks.com

UNIT 1: PARTS OF SPEECH

OPERATION 1: PARTS OF SPEECH REVIEW

FAST FACTS

Common nouns can refer to many different people, places, or things. Directions (east, west), seasons (spring, fall), and most dog breeds (poodle, labrador) are common nouns.

Proper nouns are capitalized as they name specific people, places, or things. Nicknames that replace names (Billy the Kid), positions and places that are part of a name (President Kennedy, State Street), and names derived from proper nouns (Irish setter) are proper nouns.

Pronouns take the place of nouns to make communication less repetitive.

1. The personal pronouns are I, you, he, she, it, we, they, me, him, her, us, and them.
2. The possessive pronouns show belonging (*my, our, your, his, her, its, whose,* and *their*).
2a. The independent possessive pronoun forms (*mine, ours, yours, his, hers, its, and theirs*) are used without nouns, often at the end of the sentence.
3. Possessive pronouns never use apostrophes. Do not mistake contractions (shortened forms of words) for possessive pronouns.
4. Possessive nouns are formed by adding *'s*, even if the singular noun ends in *s*.
4a. If the plural noun ends in *s*, add only the apostrophe.

Adjectives describe the kind and quantity of a noun.

1. Adjectives are often used to describe the five senses: sight, hearing, smell, taste, and touch.
2. Adjectives also indicate the number or amount of a noun.
3. Article adjectives come before a noun to specify which one. There are three article adjectives—*a*, *an*, and *the*.
   3a. *An* should be used with nouns beginning with a vowel sound (short and long sounds of *a, e, i, o,* and *u*).
   3b. *A* should be used with nouns beginning with a consonant sound (all but the vowel sounds).
3c. *The* can be used with any noun.

Write an example sentence about books using the part of speech indicated in the chart below. Then turn the page to continue your review.

proper noun	
independent possessive pronoun	
possessive plural noun	
sensory adjective	
article AND number/amount adjective	

FAST FACTS

Verbs can be classified as transitive or intransitive.

1. **Transitive verbs** transfer action to an object, or they don't make sense in the sentence. The verbs *pay*, *have*, *write*, *off*, *bring*, *borrow*, *raise*, and *discuss* are always transitive.
2. **Intransitive verbs** don't require an object to make sense in the sentence and may come at the end of the sentence. The verbs *arrive*, *die*, *sit*, *laugh*, *increase*, and *vote* are always intransitive.
3. Some verbs can be transitive or intransitive, depending on whether there is an object of action in the sentence. If you aren't sure, check a dictionary.

Adverbs describe actions in terms of how, when, and where. Adverbs can modify verbs, adjectives, or other adverbs.

Adverbs frequently end in *-ly*, but some adverbs are spelled the same way as adjectives. When there is an *-ly* adverb, use it instead of the adjective form when describing an action.

A **preposition** is a word that connects with a noun or pronoun in terms of direction, time, place, space, or things.

1. Avoid using unnecessary prepositions (that don't add information).
2. You may end a sentence with a preposition to be less formal.

Coordinating conjunctions join the same parts of speech or sentence elements with equal importance (nouns, verbs, adjectives, adverbs). These conjunctions are *for*, *and*, *nor*, *but*, *or*, *yet*, and *so*. The easiest way to remember them is with the acronym FANBOYS.

1. It is grammatically correct to begin a sentence with a conjunction if the sentence is complete (includes a subject, verb, and a complete idea).

An **interjection** is a grammatically independent word or group of words commonly used to express a sudden emotion (Oh! Ouch!). They are often followed by an exclamation point and are not typically used in professional communication.

Write the part of speech of the underlined word in the sentence.

Part of Speech	Sentence
	The book *Calvin & Hobbes* <u>gave</u> me the giggles as a kid.
	All the books <u>on</u> the shelf are mine.
	The books' pages have many highlights <u>and</u> annotations.
	<u>My goodness</u>, how I enjoy reviewing those yellow notes.
	<u>Later</u> I'll show you some of my favorites.

CLIENT Y

MISSION 1: Your client was asked to send you a series of text messages, introducing himself. Highlight 15 errors in the messages.

1. Wow. Its exciting to be a client for fast grammar.
2. I was asked to send messages but wasn't sure where to.
3. So giving it a try.
4. This is a amazing idea.
5. I hope you can correct my grammar easy.
6. My friend and I run a Social media business.
7. This Fall we want to add more clients.
8. I'm the Founder of our company.
9. I have a sister in your program, and we have two Beagles.
10. Both beagle's nickname is couch potato.

MISSION 2: Review the grammar graphics below. We will respond to your client with the text messages that follow. Add the correct word to each blank.

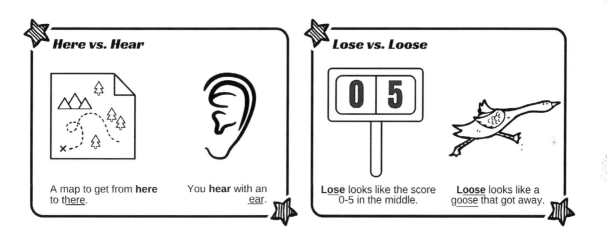

Here vs. Hear

A map to get from **here** to t**here**.

You **hear** with an ear.

Lose vs. Loose

Lose looks like the score 0-5 in the middle.

Loose looks like a goose that got away.

1. We're happy to _____ that you're excited!

2. _____ at Fast Grammar, we want happy clients.

3. Our trainees get to know grammar and their clients before we turn them _____.

4. With our technology's superiority over autocorrection, you can't _____.

5. But if you have any issues, we want to _____ about them.

MISSION 3: Review the graphic your client created for Fast Grammar. For each <u>underlined</u> word in the graphic, highlight the original word or its correction below. Then highlight its part of speech or "neither."

fast Grammar

Hear are 5 reasons to try Fast Grammar's human autocorrection service:

1. **Saves time.** Fixing <u>autocorrections'</u> mistakes takes time you don't have.
2. **Accuracy.** Fast <u>grammar</u> is correct 99.5% of the time.
3. **Saves embarrassment.** Ugh! Human autocorrectors know what you mean to say. <u>You</u> won't look foolish or insult someone.
4. **Easy to use.** Text <u>your</u> autocorrector once a week and <u>soon</u> grammar mistakes will be replaced in real time.
5. **You have nothing to <u>loose</u>!** Fast Grammar <u>offers</u> a free trial. If it doesn't work <u>for</u> you, cancel <u>any</u> time.

Correction	Part of Speech
Hear Here	transitive verb intransitive verb neither
autocorrections' autocorrection's	possessive pronoun proper noun neither
grammar Grammar	proper noun adjective neither
You Your	personal pronoun possessive pronoun neither
your you	personal pronoun possessive pronoun neither
soon sooner	adverb adjective neither
loose lose	transitive verb preposition neither
offers offer's	transitive verb intransitive verb neither
for but	preposition conjunction neither
any many	interjection adjective neither

MISSION 4: Message Client Y about your family and Fast Grammar training so far, using an interjection.

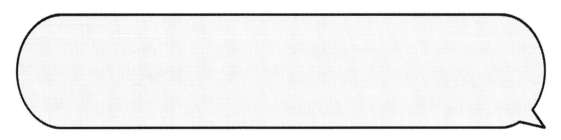

OPERATION 2: CONCRETE VS. ABSTRACT NOUNS

Abstract nouns are concepts, ideas, experiences, traits, qualities, feelings, and states of being that cannot be experienced with the five senses.

Concrete nouns are the opposite of abstract nouns and can be seen, heard, smelled, tasted, or touched.

If you aren't sure whether an abstract noun is a noun, replace it with a concrete noun in a sentence. If it makes sense, it's a noun. For example, I lost my joy. Replace the word *joy* with the concrete noun *necklace*. Because I lost my necklace. makes sense, *joy* is a noun.

Some nouns, like *death*, may be difficult to classify as abstract or concrete. *Child* is a concrete noun, but *childhood* is abstract.

Writers should use concrete nouns to explain abstract nouns in their writing to make their meaning clear.

Write another example of each type of abstract noun in the chart below. Then turn the page to review other examples.

Abstract Noun Category	Example
Emotions/Feelings - love	
Character Traits/States of Being - honesty	
Concepts/Ideas - truth	
Events/Experiences - leisure	

Review the examples of each abstract noun category below. Then using the lines that follow, write a sentence including an abstract noun that you hadn't considered as an example.

Emotions/Feelings
Sadness
Happiness
Anger
Peace

Character Traits/States of Being
Beauty
Integrity
Bravery
Skill

Concepts/Ideas
Liberty
Faith
Dream
Belief

Events/Experiences
Friendship
Culture
Education
Progress

_____

_____

_____

_____

CLIENT Z

MISSION 1: Client Z was asked to send you a series of text messages, introducing herself. Highlight the 11 ABSTRACT NOUNS in the client's texts below.

1. Hello! I want to tell you more about my hopes for this program.
2. Writing is happiness for me. But I need to improve my grammar and spelling.
3. My dream is to become an investigative journalist.
4. I need an excellent English score on my college test to make that happen.
5. I also need to improve my grammar skills.
6. But writing truth is most important to me.
7. I have made progress in my writing, but I still have things to learn.
8. Besides my education, friendship is a priority.
9. In college, I hope to meet other journalism students who write with bravery.
10. I believe that integrity creates beauty. I hope you agree.

MISSION 2: Review the grammar graphics below. We will respond to your client with the text messages that follow. Add the correct word from the graphics to each blank. Also choose from *here/hear*.

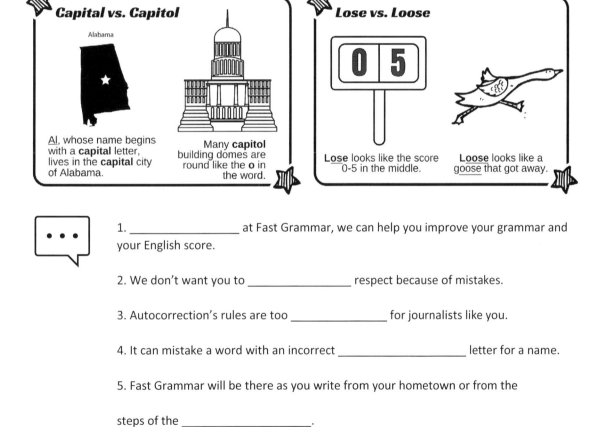

Capital vs. Capitol

Alabama

<u>Al</u>, whose name begins with a **capital** letter, lives in the **capital** city of Alabama.

Many **capitol** building domes are round like the **o** in the word.

Lose vs. Loose

Lose looks like the score 0-5 in the middle.

Loose looks like a <u>goose</u> that got away.

1. _____ at Fast Grammar, we can help you improve your grammar and your English score.

2. We don't want you to _____ respect because of mistakes.

3. Autocorrection's rules are too _____ for journalists like you.

4. It can mistake a word with an incorrect _____ letter for a name.

5. Fast Grammar will be there as you write from your hometown or from the

steps of the _____ .

MISSION 3: Client Z wants you to read her article about integrity in journalism. Please highlight the needed changes in the column on the right.

A recent <u>gallup poll</u> found that 60% of
1

Americans have little to no trust in the news. Instead,

a majority of those polled

say they see political <u>bias</u> that poses
2

a threat to democracy. Integrity is the key to

restoring trust in the news.

Here's how <u>the community times</u>
3

will demonstrate that integrity. We will

adopt clear <u>policy's</u> for the following:
4

- fact-checking
- printing corrections
- declaring funding sources

We want to restore our <u>reader's</u> trust by
5

getting the facts right, printing articles from

diverse political perspectives, and employing

multiple ombudsmen who critique our work.

With consistency in demonstrated

<u>integrity</u>, we hope to restore your trust in
6

the media.

1. A. NO CHANGE
   B. Gallup Poll
   C. Gallup poll
   D. Gallup polls

2. A. NO CHANGE
   B. Bias
   C. bias's
   D. biasis

3. A. NO CHANGE
   B. The Community Times
   C. The Community Time's
   D. the Community times

4. A. NO CHANGE
   B. Policy's
   C. Policies
   D. policies

5. A. NO CHANGE
   B. readers'
   C. Reader's
   D. Readers'

6. Which is a concrete example of integrity in the article?
   A. There are NONE
   B. bias
   C. declaring funding sources
   D. democracy

MISSION 4: Text Client Z the name of a news source that you believe demonstrates integrity, capitalizing it. Share another abstract noun that's important to you without capitalizing it.

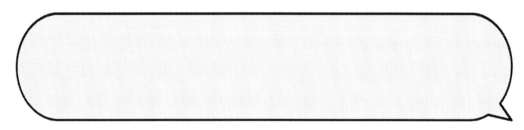

OPERATION 3: INTERROGATIVE & DEMONSTRATIVE PRONOUNS

FAST FACTS

The five interrogative pronouns are used to ask questions.

1. They are *who, whom, what,* and *which*. The possessive pronoun *whose* may also be used as an interrogative pronoun. The answer to the question is the antecedent, but it may be unknown.
1a. *Who, whom,* and *whose* are used to ask questions about people.
1b. *What* and *which* are used to ask questions about people or things.

2. The suffix *-ever* may be added to interrogative pronouns to show surprise or confusion.

3. The demonstrative pronouns *this, that, these,* and *those* refer to specific nouns.
3a. *This* is used for something nearby, and *that* is used for something at a distance.
3b. *These* is the plural form of *this* and *those* is the plural form of *that*.
3c. Do not add *here* or *there* to a demonstrative pronoun and do not use *them* in place of *these* or *those*.

Write the rule number that each sentence in the chart below is an example of. The first one is done for you. When you are finished, turn the page to see if you were correct.

Rule Number	Example sentence
1a	**Who** took my pen?
	This here is my pen. - incorrect
	Whatever did you think you were doing?
	This is the pen I've had since 7th grade.
	Those are my shoes.

Review the examples for each pronoun rule below. Then in the table that follows, write another example sentence using the pronoun for the rule indicated.

1a. Who, whom, and *whose* are used to ask questions about people.

Who took my pen?
To **whom** is the letter addressed?

1b. What and *which* are used to ask questions about people or things.

What is for dinner?

2. The suffix -ever may be added to interrogative pronouns to show surprise or confusion.

Whatever did you think you were doing?

3. The demonstrative pronouns *this, that, these,* and *those* refer to specific nouns.
3a. This is used for something nearby, and *that* is used for something at a distance.

This is the pen I've had since 7th grade.

3b. These is the plural form of *this* and *those* is the plural form of *that*.

Whose shoes are **those**?

3c. Do not add *here* or *there* to a demonstrative pronoun and do not use *them* in place of *these* or *those*.

This here is my pen. - incorrect
Them are my shoes. – incorrect

Pronoun/Rule	Example Sentence
whose/1a	
which/1b	
who/2	
that/3a	
these/3b	

CLIENT Y

MISSION 1: We asked Client Y to text you about his week. Highlight the 10 INTERROGATIVE AND DEMONSTRATIVE PRONOUNS he used.

1. Thanks for your help last week. Now what is the next step?
2. This is the part of the program I don't understand.
3. Like who will take over for my autocorrector when he or she finishes Fast Grammar?
4. What is the privacy policy for my communication?
5. If my sister and I both have requests, whose is handled first?
6. That is what I need to know to feel comfortable.
7. And when does the program end?
8. Which of the grammar errors do you see most?
9. Whatever will I do if Fast Grammar cancels their program?
10. These are a few more questions I have for you.

MISSION 2: Review the grammar graphics below. We will respond to your client with the text messages that follow. Add the correct word from the graphics. Also choose from *lose/loose*.

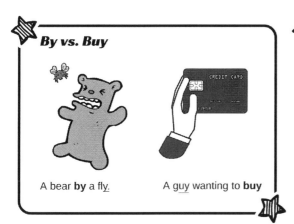

By vs. Buy

A bear **by** a fly.

A guy wanting to **buy**

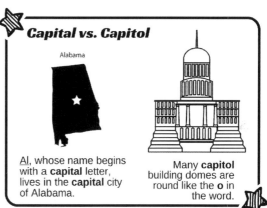

Capital vs. Capitol

Alabama

Al, whose name begins with a **capital** letter, lives in the **capital** city of Alabama.

Many **capitol** building domes are round like the **o** in the word.

1. When your autocorrector finishes training, you will not _____ our services.

2. To reassure you, we are not _____ with your personal information.

3. We have a strict privacy policy agreed to _____ your autocorrector.

4. When you _____ access to the Fast Grammar program, you aren't competing for help.

5. One thing your autocorrector will look for is proper nouns without

_____ letters.

MISSION 3: Client Y created the poster on the left to advertise his business. Rewrite the copy correctly on the blank poster on the right.

MISSION 4: Find a persuasive ad that correctly uses the word *buy* and write its text in the box below. We will share it with Client Y to reassure him he isn't alone in making errors.

OPERATION 4: NOUNS & PRONOUNS AS ADJECTIVES

FAST FACTS

Nouns that describe other nouns are known as adjectival nouns.
a *popular* magazine – *magazine* is described by the adjective *popular*
a *tennis* magazine – *magazine* is described by the noun *tennis*

1. Adjectival nouns are not possessive nouns and do not require apostrophes.
Presidents Day, not *Presidents' Day,* as the day is in honor of presidents, not owned by them.

2. Adjectival nouns are usually singular, but there are exceptions.
I read magazines when I check out *library* books. (not *libraries*)
I love *sports* magazines. (not *sport*)

3. Adjectival nouns may become hyphenated or compound nouns.
Being involved in sports has helped my *self-esteem.*
I do my stretching routine in the *bedroom.*

4. Multiple adjectival nouns may be used to modify a noun.
The *Australia tennis team* coach featured in the magazine teaches a two-handed backhand.

5. An adjective may be used in conjunction with an adjectival noun.
The *new Australia tennis team* coach was a top doubles player.

Pronouns that can function as adjectives are:
1. possessive (*my, our, your, his, her, its,* whose, and *their*)

2. interrogative (*who, whom, what,* and *which*)

3. demonstrative (*this, that, these,* and *those*)

4. indefinite (*all, any, each, few, many, several, some*)

Write an example sentence about magazines for each type of pronoun used as adjectives in the spaces above. Then turn the page to compare your examples to those given.

Review the examples below. Then write about a magazine you have read or would like to read, using a noun as an adjective.

Pronouns that can function as adjectives are:
1. possessive (*my, our, your, his, her, its,* whose, and *their*)

I look forward to *my* tennis magazine every month.

2. interrogative (*who, whom, what,* and *which)*

Which magazines do you get?

3. demonstrative (*this, that, these,* and *those*)

This issue is the most recent.

4. indefinite (*all, any, each, few, many, several, some*)

Few magazines are available in print today.

Type of magazine that interests me:

CLIENT Z

MISSION 1: We asked Client Z to text you about her week. Highlight the 11 ADJECTIVAL NOUNS she used.

1. You won't believe what happened to my dad's sports car.

2. It was stolen from the lot by our apartment complex.

3. Two teens who are too young to drive broke the window and started it without a key.

4. The police officer who took the report told us we were unlikely to get the car back.

5. But my mother posted a picture of the car on social media and someone had seen it!

6. We got the car and took it to an auto repair shop.

7. We heard from our insurance company agent that these thefts were on the rise.

8. My father was given a courtesy car to drive.

9. Then he got a shocking phone call.

10. His repaired sports car had been stolen again from the auto shop!

MISSION 2: Review the grammar graphics below. We will respond to your client with the text messages that follow. Add the correct word from the graphics or use *here/hear* or *lose/loose*.

Breath vs. Breathe

When you hold your **breath**, you don't see the **e**. When you **breathe**, you do see the **e**.

By vs. Buy

A bear **by** a fly. A guy wanting to **buy**

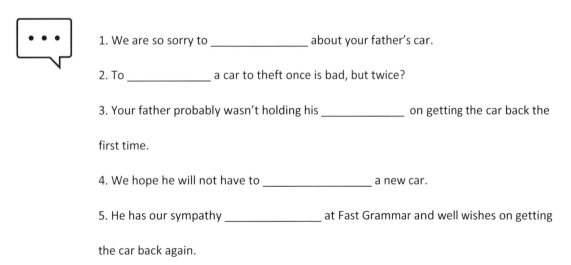

1. We are so sorry to _____ about your father's car.

2. To _____ a car to theft once is bad, but twice?

3. Your father probably wasn't holding his _____ on getting the car back the

first time.

4. We hope he will not have to _____ a new car.

5. He has our sympathy _____ at Fast Grammar and well wishes on getting

the car back again.

MISSION 3: Client Z wants you to review part of her article about auto theft. Please highlight the corrections to be made on the right and answer the question that follows.

The Forest Park Police Department reports an 85% increase in

<u>Auto thefts</u>. The majority of the increase has been blamed on a design
1

flaw in some car models. My father's sports car was stolen twice!

1. A. NO CHANGE
   B. auto theft's
   C. auto Thefts
   D. auto thefts

Viral videos show kids how to start these <u>cars models,</u> using only a
2

USB cord. Many of the thieves are too young for a <u>driver license</u>,
3

yet they are committing a crime that would be a felony in many states.

2. A. NO CHANGE
   B. car models
   C. cars' models
   D. Car models

3. A. NO CHANGE
   B. driver's license
   C. Driver License
   D. Driver's license

The auto manufacturers most affected by these thefts have been

working to develop <u>software updates</u> that will prevent the USB bypass
4

from working. However, some car owners aren't ready to <u>breath</u> with
5

relief. Instead, they are expressing their frustration with the situation,

questioning why the automakers did not anticipate this security

vulnerability and take steps to address it earlier. Some have even filed

lawsuits against the companies.

4. A. NO CHANGE
   B. Software update
   C. Software updates
   D. software's update

5. A. NO CHANGE
   B. breathe
   C. breathing
   D. breaths

In the meantime, authorities are urging <u>car owners</u> to <u>by</u>
6   7

steering wheel locks, use GPS tracking systems, and park in well-lit

areas. My father will be purchasing another car model.

6. A. NO CHANGE
   B. car's owners
   C. cars' owners
   D. Car owners

7. A. NO CHANGE
   B. buy
   C. bye
   D. own

How many of the underlined words/phrases above include adjectival nouns?

8. A. NONE
   B. 2
   C. 4
   D. 6

MISSION 4: In the text bubble below, ask Client Z a question about her article. Use an interrogative adjective.

OPERATION 5: VERB CONJUGATION

Conjugating a verb means adding a subject and tense to its infinitive form (to + verb). Choosing the correct verb through proper conjugation helps make writing clear.

Subjects of sentences vary in person (known in literature as point of view) and number.

1. <u>First person</u> uses the pronouns *I* (singular) and *we* (plural). The narrator in a story is giving a personal point of view.

2. <u>Second person</u> uses the pronoun *you* (singular or plural) or *you* is the assumed subject as in a command.

3. <u>Third person</u> uses the pronouns *he, she, it* (singular) and *they* (plural). The narrator is telling the story as an observer.

Tense describes the time of the verb's action. Verbs are regular and have a past tense form ending in *-ed* or are irregular and form the past tense in another way.

1. <u>Present tense</u> verbs are occurring now. Present tense forms of *to be* include *is, am,* and *are.* When combined with the *-ing* form of another verb, they are helping verbs that indicate present tense. Present tense verbs without helping verbs end in *–s* for singular subjects and have no ending for plural subjects.

2. <u>Past tense</u> verbs occurred earlier. They end in *–d* or *–ed* for regular verbs.

3. <u>Future tense</u> verbs are yet to occur. *Will* or *shall* are used with the verb in the future tense.

Aspect describes the nature of the verb's action:

1. <u>Simple</u> (the action is happening now)

2. <u>Perfect</u> (the action is finished). Perfect tense uses the helping verbs *has, have,* or *had* plus the past participle. A past participle is a past tense form of a verb, usually ending in *-ed, -d, -t, -en,* or *–n.* Common errors are choosing the wrong past participle or using it without the helping verb.

3. <u>Progressive</u> (the action is ongoing). The progressive tense is constructed of the helping verb *be* plus the present participle form of the verb (*-ing*).

4. <u>Perfect Progressive</u> (the action was ongoing but is now finished.) The perfect progressive tense uses the helping verb *have* with *been* and the *-ing* form of the verb.

Subject	Tense	Progressive	Standard
1st Person S	Present	I **am reading** the book.	I **read** the book.
1st Person P	Past	We **were reading** the book.	We **read** the book.
2nd Person	Future	You **will be reading** the book.	You **will read** the book.
3rd Person S	Present Perfect	She **has been reading** the book.	She **has read** the book.
3rd Person S	Past Perfect	He **had been reading** the book.	He **had read** the book.
3rd Person P	Future Perfect	They **will have been reading** the book.	They **will have read** the book.

Using the example chart on the previous page as a guide, complete the verb conjugation charts below for the verbs <u>to eat</u> and <u>to give</u>.

to eat

Subject	Tense	Progressive	Standard
1st Person S	Present		
1st Person P	Past		
2nd Person	Future		
3rd Person S	Present Perfect		
3rd Person S	Past Perfect		
3rd Person P	Future Perfect		

to give

Subject	Tense	Progressive	Standard
1st Person S	Present		
1st Person P	Past		
2nd Person	Future		
3rd Person S	Present Perfect		
3rd Person S	Past Perfect		
3rd Person P	Future Perfect		

CLIENT Y

MISSION 1: We asked Client Y to text you about his week. Highlight the 4 sentences in PERFECT OR PERFECT PROGRESSIVE TENSE.

1. You saved me with the edits to my poster. Thank you!
2. I have been making a lot of grammar mistakes.
3. And I had reviewed the poster before sending.
4. But I obviously missed some errors.
5. Now I'm wondering about lost business due to my grammar.
6. But I've heard my grandma say, "No use crying over spilled milk."
7. And I've heard my dad say, "Onward and upward."
8. So I guess I will try to learn from you going forward.
9. I hope to make more money because I'm your client.
10. But you don't guarantee that, right?

MISSION 2: Review the grammar graphics below. We will respond to your client with the text messages that follow. Add the correct word from the graphics or use *by/buy*.

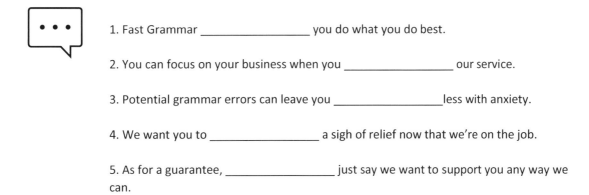

1. Fast Grammar _____ you do what you do best.

2. You can focus on your business when you _____ our service.

3. Potential grammar errors can leave you _____less with anxiety.

4. We want you to _____ a sigh of relief now that we're on the job.

5. As for a guarantee, _____ just say we want to support you any way we can.

MISSION 3: Review the product landing page your client created for a customer. Review the <u>underlined</u> words and <mark>highlight</mark> the change or answer for each on the right.

Virtual Pickleball <u>will be</u> the fast-paced, futuristic game that keeps players on their toes with a simulated ball of light that bounces off the walls and ceiling. It's the spaced-out version of pickleball you can play in your living room.	**1. will be** a. NO CHANGE b. is c. was
How to Play Playing Virtual Pickleball is easy! Use your electronic "racquet" to return the ball ... or play solo against the game console. Scorekeeping is automatic. The first one to 11 wins! But the game is so much fun, you can't <u>loose</u>. <u>Simply turn on the game console, grab your racquet, and "hit" the ball.</u> The game is designed with beginners in mind, so you can start playing right away!	**2. loose** a. NO CHANGE b. lose c. loss **3. The sentence is in:** a. 1st person b. 2nd person c. 3rd person
What's Included Virtual Pickleball includes everything you need. It comes with 2 racquets, so you can start playing with a friend or family member immediately. The game console is compact and easy to set up.	
Benefits of Playing Virtual Pickleball People who play Virtual Pickleball <u>have saw</u> many benefits. It's a great way to get some exercise while having fun. You can play with friends or family members, and it's suitable for all ages. It's also a great way to improve your hand-eye coordination and reflexes. And you can stay home to play this popular game. No more waiting for a court!	**4. have saw** a. NO CHANGE b. saw c. have seen d. seen **5. let's** a. NO CHANGE b. let us c. lets
Buy Now Don't wait to get your hands on this exciting new game. Virtual Pickleball <u>let's</u> you play with friends and family indoors. And it will be the best gift you <u>have ever gave</u>. Order now and start playing today!	**6. have ever gave** a. NO CHANGE b. have gave c. have ever given d. ever given

MISSION 4: In the text bubble below, tell the client how you'd suggest playing this game to your family using the word *let's*.

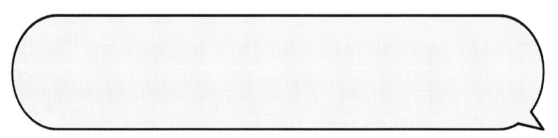

⚡ OPERATION 6: PROBLEMATIC VERB PAIRS

The meaning of the verbs *lie/lay*, *sit/set*, and *rise/raise* are commonly confused.
Lie, *sit*, and *rise* are intransitive verbs with no objects.
Lay, *set*, and *raise* are transitive verbs that require an object of the action.

Some tricks to remember the difference are:

Lie = recline; lay = place. The word and its meaning have the same vowel sound.

A dog <u>sits</u> where you <u>set</u> his bowl.

You <u>rise</u> to <u>raise</u> your glass.

The past tense of these verbs can add to the confusion. See the chart below.

Present	Past
lie	lay
lay	laid
sit	sat
set	set
rise	rose
raise	raised

Write an example sentence about sleep for each present tense verb in the chart below. Then check your examples against those given on the next page.

Present Tense Verb	Sentence About Sleep
lie	
lay	
sit	
set	
rise	
raise	

Review the examples to make sure you were correct. Then complete the chart with the Past Tense Verb (Present Tense is in parentheses).

Present Tense Verb	Sentence About Sleep
lie	I lie down an hour before bed.
lay	I lay my clothes out for the next day before I go to sleep.
sit	I sit up too late watching movies before I go to sleep.
set	I set my alarm clock every night.
rise	I rise without hitting the snooze button.
raise	I raise the shade to help me wake up.

Past Tense Verb	Sentence About Sleep
lay (lie)	
laid (lay)	
(sat) sit	
set (set)	
rose (rise)	
raised (raise)	

CLIENT Z

MISSION 1: We asked Client Z to text you about her week. Highlight the 3 INCORRECT VERBS she used in the messages.

1. Ever since my dad's car was stolen, I've had trouble sleeping.
2. I laid down at the usual time.
3. But I keep thinking I hear something.
4. I raise up and look out the window.
5. When I see nothing, I set down and try to relax.
6. I get back into bed, but I'm wired.
7. My dad set up a video security system.
8. The system raised my hopes that I'd be able to sleep.
9. But I still can't lay my head on the pillow and sleep through the night.
10. I make sure I've set my alarm and laid out my clothes, but I'm late rising.

MISSION 2: Review the grammar graphics below. We will respond to your client with the text messages that follow. Add the correct word from the graphics or from *breath/breathe*.

Have vs. Of

I can **have** a whole cookie ...
(possess) *verb*

or a bite **of** cookie.
(part of whole)
preposition

Let's vs. Lets

Let's get matching Us shirts. (let us)
contraction
suggestion

I don't let Max sit on the couch, but my brother always **lets** him. (allows)
present tense
3rd person singular

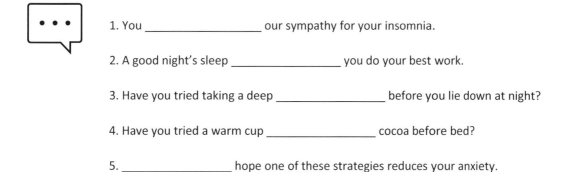

1. You _____ our sympathy for your insomnia.

2. A good night's sleep _____ you do your best work.

3. Have you tried taking a deep _____ before you lie down at night?

4. Have you tried a warm cup _____ cocoa before bed?

5. _____ hope one of these strategies reduces your anxiety.

MISSION 3: Review the essay your client wrote about sleep. Highlight necessary corrections to underlined words as indicated in the right column.

Sleep plays a vital role in the physical and mental well-being of teenagers. I've learned that the hard way since my dad's <u>sports' car</u> was stolen. However, many kids my age find it difficult to get enough sleep due to academic demands, social activities, and screen time. These are some tips I'll be following to get enough z's.	**1. sports' car** a. NO CHANGE b. sport's car c. sports car
Establish a Consistent Sleep Schedule: We should aim to go to bed and wake up at the same time each day, even on weekends. That seems crazy, but doctors say that having a regular time to <u>lay</u> down will work with our circadian rhythm and not against it.	**2. lay** a. NO CHANGE b. lie c. laid
Create a Sleep-Friendly Environment: Our sleep environment should be relaxing. This means keeping the bedroom cool, dark, and quiet. Minimizing the use of electronic devices, such as smartphones and laptops, before bedtime can also improve sleep quality. I have a bad habit of using screens before I sleep and as soon as I <u>rise</u>.	**3. rise** a. NO CHANGE b. raise c. risen
Practice Relaxation Techniques: Deep breathing exercises and reading a print book can promote a calm and peaceful state of mind, making it easier to fall asleep. I have also found it helpful to journal. I write out my worries and an action to take for each. I <u>sit</u> the journal aside and feel less stressed.	**4. sit** a. NO CHANGE b. sat c. set
Limit Stimulants and Large Meals: When you've had trouble sleeping, caffeine could <u>of</u> been the problem. We should avoid caffeinated drinks, particularly in the afternoon and evening, as they can interfere with falling asleep. Many experts also recommend eating small amounts within three hours of bedtime, so Indigestion is less likely to keep us up.	**5. of** a. NO CHANGE b. had c. have
Getting enough sleep is required for teens to function at their best. <u>Lets</u> see if establishing a consistent sleep schedule, creating a sleep-friendly environment, practicing relaxation techniques, and limiting caffeine and large meals will help us get the sleep we need.	**6. Lets** a. NO CHANGE b. Let's c. Lets'

MISSION 4: In the text bubble below, write which sleep tip you will try and why. Use one of the problematic verbs you learned.

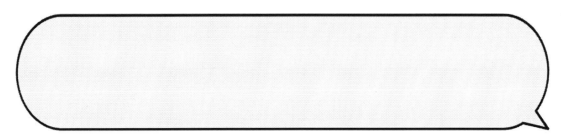

OPERATION 7: ADJECTIVE OR ADVERB

Adjectives and adverbs are both modifiers. When choosing a modifier, determine the part of speech being modified.

Adjectives modify nouns or pronouns (number, kind, which one).
Adverbs modify verbs, adverbs, and adjectives (where, when, how).

Some adverbs are formed by adding -ly to an adjective:
Easy/easily

Slow/slowly

Real/really

Calm/calmly

Bad/badly

Adjectives follow linking verbs (am, are, feel, seem).
Good is an adjective.

Well can be an adjective (meaning in good health) or adverb (meaning expertly).

Write example sentences about friendship for each *-ly* adverb in the spaces above. Also write sentences with *good* as an adjective and *well* as an adverb. Underline the modified word in each sentence. Check the examples on the next page.

Review the examples to make sure you were correct. Then use each word in a sentence as the opposite part of speech in the chart that follows.

Some adverbs are formed by adding -ly to an adjective:
Easy/easily
I <u>make</u> friends easily.

Slow/slowly
Some of my friendships <u>developed</u> slowly.

Real/really
One of my really <u>close</u> friends is my neighbor.

Calm/calmly
We <u>talk</u> through any conflicts calmly.

Bad/badly
But I've <u>handled</u> conflicts badly in the past.

Adjectives follow linking verbs (am, are, feel, seem).
Good is an adjective.
My neighbor has been a good <u>friend</u> since childhood.

Well can be an adjective (meaning in good health) or adverb (meaning expertly).
I want to <u>manage</u> my friendships well.

easy	
slow	
real	
calm	
bad	
well	

CLIENT Y

MISSION 1: We asked Client Y to text you about his week. Highlight the 4 ADJECTIVES or ADVERBS he used incorrectly in the messages.

1. My friend and business partner and I aren't getting along well.
2. He doesn't feel good about our focus.
3. He says he can create graphics easy.
4. But landing pages like the Virtual Pickleball one are really hard for him.
5. I used a calm voice, but he was real upset.
6. He wants to build the business more slow than I do.
7. He says we can limit our focus and still make money easily.
8. I want to get lots of jobs until we really know our specialty.
9. I feel badly that we aren't getting along.
10. But for now we see our business differently.

MISSION 2: Review the grammar graphics below. We will respond to your client with the text messages that follow. Add the correct word from the graphics or from *let's/lets*.

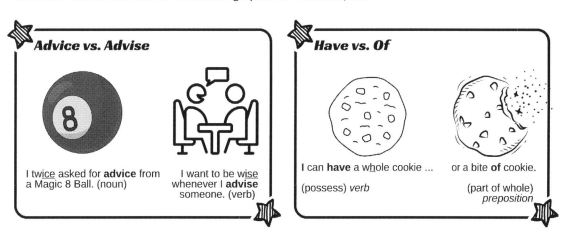

Advice vs. Advise

I twice asked for **advice** from a Magic 8 Ball. (noun)

I want to be wise whenever I **advise** someone. (verb)

Have vs. Of

I can **have** a whole cookie ...

(possess) *verb*

or a bite **of** cookie.

(part of whole) *preposition*

1. We know you didn't ask for our _____ on your business.

2. We could _____ asked for your permission to offer it first.

3. But if one business partner _____ the other have his way,

4. the amount _____ conflict will decrease significantly.

5. In the meantime, you could ask a business coach to _____ you.

MISSION 3: Review the email your client plans to send to a business coach. Highlight necessary corrections to underlined words as indicated in the right column.

I hope you are doing well. I have been listening to your business podcast and would love your <u>advise</u> on an important decision for the social media business my friend and I run.	**1. advise** a. NO CHANGE b. advice c. Advise
My friend and I disagree on whether to specialize <u>immediately</u> or provide lots of services to get more sales. While I understand the benefits of niching down, I'm not sure if it's the right approach since we're just getting started.	**2. immediately** a. NO CHANGE b. immediate c. quick
On one hand, specializing in a specific niche within social media (like videos) could allow us to become experts <u>quick</u>. We could also stand out from our competitors. However, I am concerned about limiting our growth potential by narrowing our focus too much.	**3. quick** a. NO CHANGE b. quickly c. of
On the other hand, I feel <u>good</u> about trying to serve a larger audience. It seems we could make more money. However, I know there is more competition if we try to do it all.	**4. good** a. NO CHANGE b. well c. badly
If you would <u>of</u> started a social media business at my age, would you have specialized in one area or no? What are the pros and cons? And do you have any tips for running a business when the partners don't agree?	**5. of** a. NO CHANGE b. had c. have
I feel <u>badly</u> for taking your time, but I greatly appreciate your recommendations. Best regards,	**6. badly** a. NO CHANGE b. bad c. well

MISSION 4: In the text bubble below, write your business recommendation to the client, using *advice/advise* **correctly.**

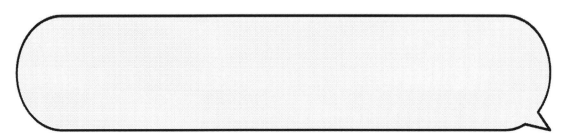

FAST FACTS

There are three forms of adjectives and adverbs used to show varying degrees of comparison: the positive, the negative, the comparative, and the superlative.

The positive form is used when the comparison is nonspecific. No change is made to the adjective/adverb.
I lifted *heavy* weights today.

The negative form is used when a subject being compared is inferior. Add the word *less* prior to the adjective.
I have been *less active* lately.

The comparative form is used when two things are being compared with each other. It uses the suffix *-er* and the word *more*.

The superlative form is when three or more things are being compared. It uses the suffix *-est* and the word *most*.

One- and Two-Syllable Comparisons
For one-syllable words ending in *-e*, simply add the rest of the suffix (*r* or *st*).
Use the word *better* or *best* for *good/well*.
For two-syllable words ending in *-y*, change the *y* to *i* before adding the suffix.
For words ending in a consonant-vowel-consonant, double the consonant before adding the suffix. (Words ending in *-w* are an exception).
Use the word *more* or *most* prior to irregular adjectives (*modern, handsome, boring*).

Three- or More Syllable Comparisons
Add the word *more* or *most* prior to words with three or more syllables and to adverbs ending in *-ly*.

Do not double the comparison. Use the suffix (-er, -est) or a word (*better*, best, *more*, *most*) but not both.

Write a comparative or superlative sentence about exercise for each adjective/adverb in the chart below.
Then turn the page to see other examples.

Adjective/Adverb	Sentence
heavy	
good	
fit	
regularly	
challenging	

Review the examples below. Then rewrite each sentence you wrote on the previous page using the opposite form of comparison. Use comparative if you wrote superlative and vice versa.

One- and Two-Syllable Comparisons

For one-syllable words ending in -*e*, simply add the rest of the suffix (*r* or *st*).

This is the nicest gym I've been in.

Use the word *better* or *best* for *good/well*.

It has a *better* layout than my last gym.

For two-syllable words ending in -*y*, change the *y* to *i* before adding the suffix.

I had my heaviest bench press ever yesterday.

For words ending in a consonant-vowel-consonant, double the consonant before adding the suffix. (Words ending in -*w* are an exception).

I think this is the fittest I've ever been.

Use the word *more* or *most* prior to irregular adjectives (*modern, handsome, boring*).

My new gym has *more modern* equipment than the last one.

Three- or More Syllable Comparisons

Add the word *more* or *most* prior to words with three or more syllables and to adverbs ending in -*ly*.

I've been doing *more challenging* workouts.

I've been working out *more regularly*.

Do not double the comparison. Use the suffix (-er, -est) or a word (*better*, best, *more*, *most*) but not both.

I'm feeling a lot *more better*. – incorrect

I'm feeling a lot *better*. – correct

Adjective/Adverb	Sentence
heavy	
good	
fit	
regularly	
challenging	

CLIENT Z

MISSION 1: We asked Client Z to text you about her week. Highlight the 6 INCORRECT COMPARISONS she used in the messages.

1. I am sleeping better and I'm glad.
2. But I'm still most anxious.
3. I thought I would feel a lot more better by now.
4. My mom suggested I exercise more.
5. She says exercise has made her feel less stressed.
6. Watching workout videos had her exercising more consistently.
7. She was getting strongest every day.
8. But the girl stopped making videos, so my mom started going to the gym oftener.
9. Now she tries to lift her best heaviest weight each time.
10. I'm thinking of going with her to get more fit and have less anxiety too.

MISSION 2: Review the grammar graphics below. We will respond to your client with the text messages that follow. Add the correct word from the graphics. Also choose from *have/of*.

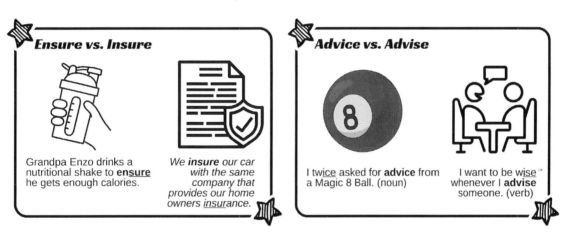

Ensure vs. Insure

Grandpa Enzo drinks a nutritional shake to **ensure** he gets enough calories.

We **insure** our car with the same company that provides our home owners insurance.

Advice vs. Advise

I twice asked for **advice** from a Magic 8 Ball. (noun)

I want to be wise whenever I **advise** someone. (verb)

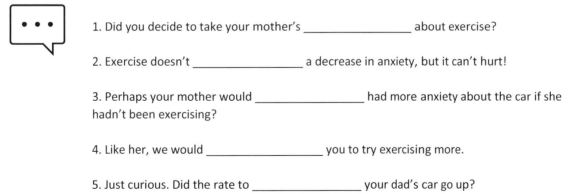

1. Did you decide to take your mother's _____ about exercise?

2. Exercise doesn't _____ a decrease in anxiety, but it can't hurt!

3. Perhaps your mother would _____ had more anxiety about the car if she hadn't been exercising?

4. Like her, we would _____ you to try exercising more.

5. Just curious. Did the rate to _____ your dad's car go up?

MISSION 3: Review the article on anxiety that your client submitted. Highlight necessary corrections to underlined words as indicated in the right column.

In a stressful, uncertain world, managing anxiety has become an even <u>more essential</u> skill. I wanted some tips to manage my own worries, so I reached out to some local mental health experts. These were their top strategies.	**1. more essential** a. NO CHANGE b. essentialer c. most essential
First, they recommended a healthy lifestyle. Regular exercise, a balanced diet, and <u>more better</u> sleep can decrease anxiety levels. Physical activity relieves muscle tension and helps us get to sleep. A healthy diet and a regular sleep schedule improve energy and productivity, giving us less to be anxious about.	**2. more better** a. NO CHANGE b. better c. betterer
A second strategy experts mentioned was self-care. This category includes activities like spending <u>less time</u> reading or watching news; having a regular quiet time for meditation, prayer, or relaxation; and dedicating time to hobbies and activities that improve mood.	**3. less time** a. NO CHANGE b.less c. lesser
A third strategy experts mentioned was social support. Talking about worries with trusted friends, family, or support groups decreases anxiety even if we don't get <u>advise</u> for specific problems.	**4. advise** a. NO CHANGE b. advice c. advises
Finally, the experts I consulted recommended seeking professional help when anxiety becomes overwhelming. Therapists and counselors can teach <u>less effective</u> techniques such as cognitive-behavioral therapy (CBT) to address underlying thought patterns and develop effective coping mechanisms.	**5. less effective** a. NO CHANGE b. effective c. most
While anxiety is even <u>more common</u> these days, these expert-recommended strategies offer a path to peace. By incorporating these techniques into our lives, we can regain control and find freedom from worry.	**6. more common** a. NO CHANGE b. commoner c. most common

MISSION 4: In the text bubble below, use a comparison correctly to talk about how you manage stress or anxiety.

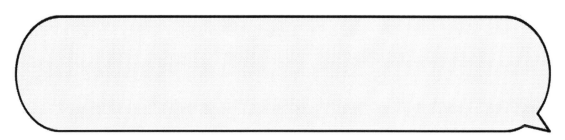

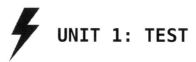 # UNIT 1: TEST

Review the Fast Facts and grammar graphic sections of Operations 1-8. Then ask your trainer for the Unit 1 test. Record your score below.

Number correct out of 50_____ x 2 = _____ %

If you didn't score as well as you hoped, complete some review exercises you can find at FunToLearnBooks.com/FastGrammar2.

UNIT 2: PARTS OF SENTENCE

OPERATION 9: PARTS OF SENTENCE REVIEW

FAST FACTS

The subject of a sentence is the noun or pronoun being described or performing the action. The subject is often, but not always, at the beginning of a sentence.

> **The simple subject** is the noun or pronoun without modifiers like adjectives.
> The diligent <u>Cassie</u> is reading again. (*The* and *diligent* are not part of the simple subject.)

The predicate of a sentence describes what the subject does with a verb, objects, and modifiers.

The simple predicate is just the verb.
Cory quickly <u>ate</u> pepperoni pizza for lunch.

A sentence includes a beginning capital letter, a subject, a predicate, a complete thought, and an end mark (period, question mark, or exclamation point).

A sentence fragment is usually missing a subject or predicate and as a result does not communicate a complete thought. They should be avoided in formal writing but are frequently used online and in fiction. Short sentences aren't necessarily fragments.

A sentence has a compound subject when two or more subjects perform the same action.
A sentence has a compound predicate when the subject is performing more than one action.
Compound subjects and predicates make writing more concise (give information in fewer words).

Compound subjects and compound predicates can be formed with coordinating conjunctions (FANBOYS). They may also be formed with the correlative conjunctions (*both/and, either/or, neither/nor, not only/but also*).

A sentence may have a compound subject <u>and</u> a compound predicate. Note that multiple subjects performing different actions is a compound sentence, not a compound subject or predicate.

Write an example sentence about communication for each sentence type. Then turn the page to continue your review.

Sentence with a compound subject	
Sentence with a compound predicate	
Sentence with a compound subject and predicate	

FAST FACTS

A double negative is a statement containing two negative words that creates confusion or has the opposite meaning of what's intended.

Negative adjectives (used before nouns) are *no, neither*.

Negative adverbs (used before verbs, adjectives, and other adverbs) are *not (-n't* in contractions), never, neither, neither/nor, **barely, hardly, scarcely, seldom, rarely**. The adverbs in bold are frequently misused in double negatives.

Negative pronouns (used in place of a noun)/[positive counterpart] are *neither [either],* nothing [anything], none [all], no one [anyone], nobody [anybody], nowhere [anywhere].

To correct a double negative with pronouns, use the corresponding positive pronoun.

Commas indicate a pause in a sentence that is briefer than a period.

Commas are used to separate a series of words or word groupings to provide clarity. The comma that precedes the word and is known as the Oxford comma and is omitted by some publications, though omission may cause confusion.

Commas are used to indicate the one being addressed or spoken to in a sentence. A comma should come before the name or nickname and after it if the name is mid-sentence.

Commas are used to separate a statement from a question in a sentence.

An appositive is a noun or pronoun (including any modifiers) that explains or identifies another noun or pronoun. An appositive usually follows the noun or pronoun but may also precede it.

If the appositive includes essential information, do not set it apart with commas.

If the sentence makes sense without the unessential appositive, set it apart with commas.

Double quotation marks are used to indicate word-for-word verbal or written quotes. Quotation marks are not used for paraphrases of what was said.

Commas are used before or after the attribution of the quote (e.g., said, reported, stated). These commas are optional with one-word quotations. Quotations used as subjects or objects may not require a comma.

Complete quotes should be capitalized. Partial quotes that complete a sentence do not require capitalization.

Double quotation marks can be used to indicate that a word is slang/jargon (used in a unique way by a particular group) or is ironic (opposite meaning). Double quotation marks should not be used to emphasize a word as with bold type. Doing so risks miscommunicating irony.

Write an example sentence about conflict resolution for each grammar concept or punctuation mark.

Negative pronoun used correctly	
Comma separating a statement from the question *do I?*	
An unessential appositive	
A quotation used as a subject	

CLIENT Y

MISSION 1: Your client sent you these text messages about his week. Highlight the concepts noted in BRACKETS in each message.

1. Didn't go well. I mean the business agreement wasn't signed. [SENTENCE FRAGMENT]
2. My friend said he couldn't hardly believe I was having him sign a legal form. [DOUBLE NEGATIVE]
3. He said "I think I should have my attorney look at this." [WORD THAT SHOULD BE FOLLOWED BY A COMMA]
4. I founded the business and asked him to be my partner. [COMPOUND PREDICATE]
5. Now he, my best friend, is treating me like I'm a con artist. [APPOSITIVE]
6. He can't sue me can he? [WORD THAT SHOULD BE FOLLOWED BY A COMMA]
7. He says we have to consider the ideas, the time and the talent we bring to the business. [WORD TO BE FOLLOWED BY AN OXFORD COMMA]
8. I kept saying, He can't be serious! [WORDS THAT SHOULD BE IN QUOTES]
9. Don't throw our friendship away over this Jack. [WORD THAT SHOULD BE FOLLOWED BY A COMMA]
10. He and I have been friends forever. I don't know what to do. [COMPOUND SUBJECT]

MISSION 2: Review the grammar graphics below. We will respond to your client with the text messages that follow. Add the correct word from the graphics or *advice/advise* to each blank.

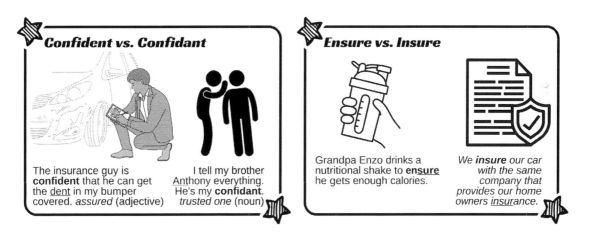

Confident vs. Confidant

The insurance guy is **confident** that he can get the <u>dent</u> in my bumper covered. *assured* (adjective)

I tell my brother Anthony everything. He's my **confidant**. *trusted one* (noun)

Ensure vs. Insure

Grandpa Enzo drinks a nutritional shake to **ensure** he gets enough calories.

*We **insure** our car with the same company that provides our home owners <u>insurance</u>.*

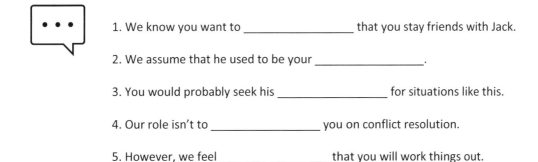

1. We know you want to _____ that you stay friends with Jack.

2. We assume that he used to be your _____.

3. You would probably seek his _____ for situations like this.

4. Our role isn't to _____ you on conflict resolution.

5. However, we feel _____ that you will work things out.

MISSION 3: Review the email to his business partner that your client submitted. Find each grammar concept indicated to the right of the paragraph and highlight it in the email. Then check the box.

Dear Jack,	
Hope you're doing well. This email might seem a bit serious, but I want to talk to you about something important. After thinking it through, I've come to the tough decision that we should end our business partnership.	☐ compound subject ☐ sentence fragment ☐ compound predicate ☐ incorrect quote ☐ should be adverb ☐ appositive ☐ wrong spelling ☐ comma should follow ☐ double negative ☐ correlative conjunction
First off, I want you to know that our friendship means a lot to me. This decision has nothing to do with how I feel about you personally. It's about what's best for Marketing Mensas.	
I think it's important for us to sit down and have an open conversation about this. Can we find a time to meet up soon? Maybe we could meet and get frozen yogurt?	
Since our friendship is "important," I want to make sure we handle this the right way. Maybe we can ask the business coach, the guy I told you about, to meet with us virtual. I am confidant he can help us reach an agreement.	
You and I could also talk to my dad's lawyer. She can tell us the right steps to end a partnership. She's said she would help me "any time." You can't never have too much advice am I right? We can figure out how to divide everything in a fair way.	
I believe that by both discussing everything openly and working together, we can wrap up our business partnership in a friendly way.	
Thanks for understanding, and let's find a time to chat soon.	
Take care,	

MISSION 4: Message Client Y about how to improve the email to his friend. Use a compound predicate.

OPERATION 10: ADVANCED PHRASES

Phrases are groups of words that function as a single unit within a sentence. They lack a subject and a verb, so they are not complete sentences. Phrases serve various purposes in a sentence, such as providing additional information, modifying nouns or verbs, or acting as a single part of speech.

There are different types of phrases.

Noun phrases (function as the subject or object in a sentence; the main component is a noun)

Verb phrases (main and helping verbs)

Adjective phrases (describe nouns; the main component is an adjective)

Adverb phrases (describe verbs, adjectives, and adverbs)

Prepositional phrases (start with a preposition and usually indicate location, time, direction, or possession).

Write an example sentence about sports, using each type of phrase in the spaces above. Then turn the page to see other examples.

Review the examples below. Then write another sentence using each type of phrase for a different sport.

Noun phrases (function as the subject or object in a sentence; the main component is a noun)
Pickleball, *a paddle sport*, has been increasing in popularity.

Verb phrases (main and helping verbs)
Pickleball *has grown* more than 39% in the past two years.

Adjective phrases (describe nouns; the main component is an adjective)
Young and old people enjoy playing pickleball.

Adverb phrases (describe verbs, adjectives, and adverbs)
New pickleball players can play *surprisingly well*.

Prepositional phrases (start with a preposition and may serve as adjective or adverb phrases)
If you're trying pickleball *for the first time,* you may become a fan.

Noun phrase	
Verb phrase	
Adjective phrase	
Adverb phrase	
Prepositional phrase	

CLIENT Z

MISSION 1: We asked Client Z to text you about her week. Highlight each PHRASE that modifies the underlined word.

1. My <u>anxiety</u> about the car theft has decreased.
2. The <u>tips</u> I wrote about have helped me.
3. Yesterday afternoon I <u>played</u> pickleball.
4. The <u>sport</u>, played with a paddle and a wiffle ball, is easy to learn.
5. A <u>line</u> near the net is called the kitchen.
6. I <u>lost</u> points for stepping into the kitchen.
7. But <u>all</u> of us had fun playing.
8. Later that night I <u>slept</u> well.
9. <u>Exercise</u>, specifically pickleball, is my sedative.
10. This nonathletic, indoorsy <u>writer</u> is actually playing a sport.

MISSION 2: Review the grammar graphics below. We will respond to your client with the text messages that follow. Add the correct word to the blank. Also choose from *ensure/insure*.

Peak vs. Peek vs. Pique

I was w<u>eak</u> but happy when I reached the **peak**. *top* (noun/adj.)

I said <u>eek</u> when I took a **peek** behind the rock. *look* (noun/verb)

With her high <u>IQ</u>, lots of topics **pique** her interest. *excite* (verb)

Confident vs. Confidant

The insurance guy is **confident** that he can get the <u>dent</u> in my bumper covered. *assured* (adjective)

I tell my brother Anthony everything. He's my **confidant**. *trusted one* (noun)

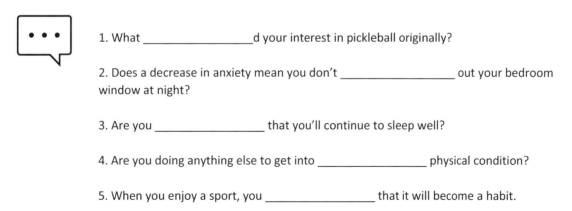

1. What _____d your interest in pickleball originally?

2. Does a decrease in anxiety mean you don't _____ out your bedroom window at night?

3. Are you _____ that you'll continue to sleep well?

4. Are you doing anything else to get into _____ physical condition?

5. When you enjoy a sport, you _____ that it will become a habit.

MISSION 3: Client Z wants you to read her article about pickleball. Please highlight the part of speech of each underlined phrase.

In a sporting revolution, pickleball has taken the nation by storm, captivating players of all ages.

This unique paddle sport has become the hottest trend in the athletic world. With its smaller court, specialized paddles, and perforated plastic ball, pickleball offers an exciting and fast-paced experience. Communities across the country are embracing this new phenomenon, witnessing a surge in participation at local community centers, parks, and recreational facilities.

What sets pickleball apart is its accessibility and inclusivity. Players of all backgrounds and athletic abilities can play. It's the perfect game for families, friends, and even retirees seeking a fun and social way to stay active.

The rise of pickleball can be attributed to its simplicity and quick learning curve. The rules are easy to understand, allowing beginners to quickly grasp the fundamentals.

In addition, pickleball offers significant health benefits. Players can have a great time while enhancing their overall well-being.

Experts predict that pickleball's popularity will only continue to soar. So, grab your paddle and start playing!

1. **In a sporting revolution**
   A. noun phrase
   B. adjective phrase
   C. prepositional phrase

2. **This unique paddle**
   A. prepositional phrase
   B. adjective phrase
   C. verb phrase

3. **at local...facilities**
   A. prepositional phrase
   B. adjective phrase
   C. verb phrase

4. **of all backgrounds**
   A. prepositional phrase
   B. noun phrase
   C. both A and B

5. **can be attributed**
   A. prepositional phrase
   B. verb phrase
   C. adjective phrase

6. **health**
   A. adjectival noun
   B. subject
   C. adverb

7. **pickleball's**
   A. possessive noun
   B. adjective
   C. both A and B

MISSION 4: Text Client Z in the bubble below whether pickleball is popular in your area using a prepositional phrase.

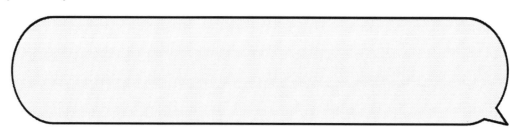

⚡ OPERATION 11: ADVANCED CLAUSES

FAST FACTS

A clause differs from a phrase in that it includes a subject and a verb. Clauses are independent (stand-alone sentences) or dependent (can only add information to the main clause).

Dependent clauses can function as:
nouns (My dog eats whatever I give him.)
adjectives (My dog eats eggs that the chickens lay.)
adverbs (My dog eats eggs when the chickens lay them.)

To confirm a clause's part of speech, substitute another noun, adjective, or adverb in its place to see if the sentence makes sense.
nouns (My dog eats **eggs**.)
adjectives (My dog eats **chicken** eggs.) – change in order but makes sense
adverbs (My dog eats eggs **early**.)

Dependent clauses are also known as subordinate clauses. They often begin with subordinating conjunctions: for, as, if, since, therefore, hence, consequently, though, due to, provided that, because, unless, once, while, when, whenever, where, wherever, before, and after.

Noun and adjective clauses (also known as relative clauses) often begin with relative pronouns: that, which, who, whom, whichever, whoever, whomever, and whose.

Identifying dependent clauses will help you avoid writing sentence fragments and will help you use commas. You've already learned that appositives (a form of adjective/relative clause) are not set off by commas when the clause is essential information but are when the clause is not.

The dog **who belongs to the neighbor** eats my chicken eggs. – essential
The neighbors' dog, **who escapes the yard daily,** eats my chicken eggs. – not essential

Most adverbial clauses should be followed by a comma at the beginning of a sentence but should not be set off by a comma at the end of a sentence.

As soon as my chickens lay eggs, the neighbors' dog eats them.
The neighbors' dog eats my chicken eggs **as soon as they lay them**.

Rewrite the sentences with phrases as sentences with clauses:

Pickleball, *a paddle sport*, has been increasing in popularity.
Young and old people alike enjoy playing pickleball.
New pickleball players can play *surprisingly well*.

53

CLIENT Y

MISSION 1: We asked Client Y to text you about his week. Highlight 5 SUBORDINATE CLAUSES in the messages.

1. I met my friend to discuss ending our partnership.
2. When I arrived at the smoothie place to meet him, I was shocked.
3. I thought the email that I sent was clear.
4. But my friend took my email as a threat.
5. He brought two people, his dad and his dad's attorney.
6. He said his opinion was whatever the two of them had to say.
7. After I adjusted to the shock, I was mad.
8. I wanted to protect the friendship by having this meeting.
9. But my friend only seemed to care about money.
10. They all threatened to sue me when I walked out the door.

MISSION 2: Review the grammar graphics below. We will respond to your client with the text messages that follow. Add the correct word to the blank. Also choose from *confident/confidant*.

Affect vs. Effect

A book can **affect** (act on) you. *-usually a verb*

One **effect** (end result) is more creativity. *-usually a noun*

Peak vs. Peek vs. Pique

I was w<u>ea</u>k but happy when I reached the **peak**. *top (noun/adj.)*

I said <u>ee</u>k when I took a **peek** behind the rock. *look (noun/verb)*

With her high <u>IQ</u>, lots of topics **pique** her interest. *excite (verb)*

1. We are sure the meeting had a terrible _____ on you.

2. We hope you won't let it _____ you too much going forward.

3. No one gets to the _____ of the mountain without going through some valleys.

4. It's disappointing when you get a _____ at a darker side of a friend.

5. But we are _____ that things will work out.

OPERATION 11: ADVANCED CLAUSES

MISSION 3: Review your client's response to the threatening letter he received. Find at least one example of each grammar concept indicated to the right of the paragraph and write the line number(s) in the email where it can be found.

1 Jack, I can't believe you had your dads lawyer, send me a letter, when I 2 was trying to work this out with you! You are apparently agreeing with 3 everything that he says.	_____noun clause _____sentence fragment _____adjective clause
4 The letter says I need to "cease and desist." I had to get the definition of 5 that. What do you want me to stop doing exactly? I'm so confused.	_____incorrect quote _____adverb clause _____comma should follow
6 The letter also says that all business assets are effectively frozen. I had to 7 look that up too! First, what business assets are you talking about? We 8 have used the little bit of money we've made to advertise the business. 9There is no money to freeze!	_____missing apostrophe _____should be an adverb _____ wrong spelling _____shouldn't have
10 The lawyer says you can sue me for damages. Again, what damages? 11 What money have you lost? I read that you can sue for pain and 12 suffering in a lawsuit. If that's true, then I have a case. I am suffering!	comma after
13 I thought we were "friends." We disagreed on the direction for the 14 business. Because we couldn't agree I felt we should end our 15 partnership. I wanted to end it and keep our friendship. But the 16 friendship that we've had for years doesn't seem to be important to you.	
17 I can't describe how bad this has effected me. I hope you'll have your 18 lawyer "cease and desist." So we can work this out.	

MISSION 4: Message Client Y about what you think he should do, using a subordinate clause.

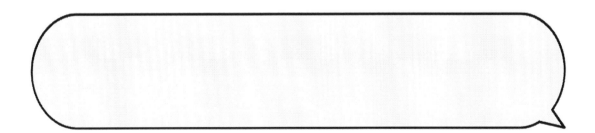

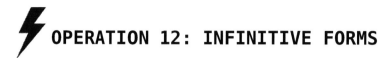 **OPERATION 12: INFINITIVE FORMS**

FAST FACTS

An infinitive is a verb form (or verbal) constructed of the word *to* plus the verb. Infinitives function as:

nouns (subjects, direct objects, subject complements)
To read is a privilege.
I love *to read*.
My joy is *to read*.

adjectives (follow nouns)
The best book *to read* is one you enjoy.

adverbs (explain why)
I lie down *to read*.

Infinitive phrases are formed when other words or phrases are added to provide more information.
I learned to read well.
I learned to read text quickly.

Infinitive forms include:
Perfect infinitive (add *have* to the past participle to show potential future completion)
I would love *to have read* the 100 top books of all time.
Progressive infinitive (add *be* to the *-ing* verb form to show continuing action)
There's nothing I enjoy more than *to be reading* in bed.
Perfect progressive (add *have been* to the *-ing* verb form to show continuing action completed)
I seem *to have been sleeping* instead of reading.

Write an example sentence about writing for each type of infinitive listed below.

<u>to write</u> as an adjective
<u>to write</u> in an infinitive phrase
<u>to write</u> as a perfect infinitive
<u>to write</u> as a progressive infinitive
<u>to write</u> as a perfect progressive infinitive

CLIENT Z

MISSION 1: We asked Client Z to text you about her week. Write the number(s) for the type of infinitive used in each message in the blank.

1 – noun, 2 – adjective, 3 – adverb, 4 – perfect, 5 – progressive, 6 – perfect progressive

1. I'd like to teach my mom to play pickleball.   _____
2. I told her that it's such a fun sport to play.   _____
3. She doesn't like to be making mistakes.   _____
4. But I told her that she needs to have played first.   _____
5. I explained that I play pickleball to relax.   _____
6. Now I won't miss my time to play.   _____
7. She says she wants to practice alone first.   _____
8. But to play is to be practicing.   _____
9. She seems to have been making excuses for weeks.   _____
10. By next week, I want to have played with her once.   _____

MISSION 2: Review the grammar graphics below. We will respond to your client with the text messages that follow. Add the correct homophone to the blank. Also choose from *peak/peek/pique*.

All ready vs. Already

Ally is **all ready** for the trip. All of her clothes are packed. (*completely prepared*)

Al **already** missed the L train and his flight is leaving **already**. (*previously; so soon*)

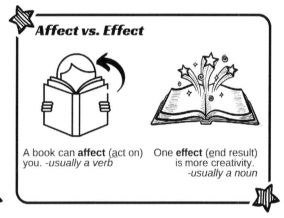

Affect vs. Effect

A book can **affect** (act on) you. -*usually a verb*

One **effect** (end result) is more creativity. -*usually a noun*

1. So you're _____ encouraging family to play pickleball? That's great!

2. Have you _____ played with your brother?

3. We are glad that pickleball has had such a positive _____ on your anxiety.

4. Perhaps you can _____ your mom's interest just by having her watch you play.

5. The _____ of modeling your enjoyment is very powerful.

MISSION 3: Review your client's essay about helping people change. Highlight the correction that should be made to each underlined portion.

Lately I've been trying to get my mom to be playing pickleball with no success. I've learned that while I cannot force her to change, I can inspire and influence her. If you'd like someone to change, these strategies may help you.

Lead by Example: The best way to inspire change in others is to live it. By consistently demonstrating positive behavior, we can become a powerful role model who encourages others to follow suit. I keep playing pickleball and telling my mom how much fun I'm having.

Empathy and Understanding: To have changed someone, we must first understand their perspective and motivations. By actively listening we make it safe for them to trust us. I have expressed understanding when my mom says she isn't athletic.

Highlight Benefits: People are more likely to welcome change when they understand the potential benefits it can bring. I have shared with my mom how playing pickleball has decreased my anxiety and increased my energy.

Support and Encouragement: Providing practical help and encouragement can be the difference in someone's willingness to change. I have told my mom that I will play with her privately and I had expressed my belief in her ability to play.

Although change is always an individual's choice, we possess the power to influence and inspire transformation in others. I had all ready used some of these strategies, but my mom just asked if I wanted to show her how to play pickleball! When we lead by example, practice empathy, highlight the benefits, and provide support, we make it easier for others to do better.

1. to be playing pickleball
a. NO CHANGE
b. to play pickleball
c. to have played pickleball

2. to inspire change
a. NO CHANGE
b. to be inspiring change
c. to have inspired change

3. To have changed
a. NO CHANGE
b. To be changing
c. To change

4. had expressed
a. NO CHANGE
b. had been expressing
c. have expressed

5. all ready
a. NO CHANGE
b. already
c. completely

6. to do better
a. NO CHANGE
b. to improve
c. to change

MISSION 4: Message Client Z about how you inspire others to change. Use an infinitive.

FAST FACTS

You have learned many uses for commas in your training already:

1. Lists of three or more items

2. When speaking directly to someone

3. To set off a direct quote

4. To set off appositives

5. To set off nonessential clauses

6. After an opening clause or phrase

7. Before a coordinating conjunction joining independent clauses

8. Before a question at the end of an independent clause

Some additional uses of commas are:

9. Following an unemotional interjection like *yes*, *no*, or *well*.

10. Following transition words and phrases like *first*, *finally*, *therefore*, and *as a result*.

11. Degrees and addresses
Kaylie Scott, MD, lives on 107 East Avenue, Cincinnati, OH 45201.

12. Dates (set off the year) and numbers (set off groups of 3)
A total of 2,390 Pearl Harbor military and civilians were killed on December 7, 1941.

Write an example sentence about history or medicine for comma uses 1-9. Then turn the page to review other examples.

Review the examples below. Then write another example sentence for comma uses 11 and 12 on the lines that follow.

1. Lists of three or more items
The Axis powers in World War II were Germany, Italy, and Japan.

2. When speaking directly to someone
"Mr. Gorbachev, tear down this wall!" – Ronald Reagan

3. To set off a direct quote
President Kennedy said, "Ask not what your country can do for you—ask what you can do for your country."

4. To set off appositives
Insulin, an essential hormone, controls blood sugar levels.

5. To set off nonessential clauses
My friend Jacob, the one who has diabetes, went camping with us.

6. After an opening clause or phrase
Before eating a big meal, Jacob checks his blood sugar.

7. Before a coordinating conjunction joining independent clauses
Jacob got a continuous glucose monitor, so his diabetes is easier to manage.

8. Before a question at the end of an independent clause
You're not going to drink soda now, are you?

Some additional uses of commas are:

9. Following an unemotional interjection like *yes*, *no*, or *well*.
No, I don't drink soda.

10. Following transition words and phrases like *first*, *finally*, *therefore*, and *as a result*.
As a result, I drink more water.

11. Degrees and addresses
Kaylie Scott, MD, lives on 107 East Avenue, Cincinnati, OH 45201.

12. Dates (set off the year) and numbers (set off groups of 3)
A total of 2,390 Pearl Harbor military and civilians were killed on December 7, 1941.

_____

_____

_____

_____

CLIENT Y

MISSION 1: We asked Client Y to text you about his week. Highlight 14 words or digits that should be followed by COMMAS in the messages.

1. I heard back from Jack my business partner.
2. He said he was just diagnosed with diabetes so that explains why he was freaking out.
3. He saw Michael Jacobs MD for a physical and got the shocking news.
4. He said "I couldn't believe it!"
5. Anyway he apologized.
6. He said he isn't going to sue me for $10000 now.
7. He said "You'll forgive me won't you?"
8. I will forgive him but can I trust him?
9. I have so many questions about his diagnosis our friendship and the business.
10. Does having diabetes a disease that causes high blood sugar explain his behavior?

MISSION 2: Review the grammar graphics below. We will respond to your client with the text messages that follow. Add the correct homophone to the blank. Also choose from *affect/effect*.

Compliment vs. Complement

I gave him a **compliment** to praise him for a job well done.

We think you're the perfect **complement** to complete our team.

All ready vs. Already

Ally is **all ready** for the trip. All of her clothes are packed. *(completely prepared)*

Al **already** missed the L train and his flight is leaving **already**. *(previously; so soon)*

1. We have to _____ you on how you're handling the conflict with your friend.

2. Have you _____ told him you need to meet and talk?

3. We do think it's possible for diabetes to _____ your friend's behavior.

4. But do you think he is a good _____ to your skills in business?

5. You should be honest about the conflict's _____ on you.

MISSION 3: Review your client's essay on diabetes for health class. Highlight the correction needed.

My friend was recently diagnosed with diabetes. I wanted to understand its <u>affect on him</u> so I did some research. The first thing I learned is that diabetes <u>been increasing</u> among teenagers. It can affect them physically, emotionally, and socially.

<u>First diabetes</u> affects teens physically. Without checking blood sugars, eating at the right times, and taking insulin, serious damage to the body can occur. Hyperglycemia <u>or high blood sugar</u> can make it difficult to concentrate, while low blood sugar can cause confusion and shakiness.

Next, there are emotional effects of diabetes. Fear of low- or high-blood-sugar episodes can be distracting. Management of the condition can take time away from studying. Feeling different may lead to self-consciousness.

Finally, there are social effects of diabetes. Diabetic teens may limit eating and exercising with friends, or they may ignore their condition <u>to hopefully fit</u> in. Isolation and uncontrolled blood sugars can make the emotional effects worse.

I <u>had all ready</u> learned that diabetes is a blood-sugar disease. Now I know what a challenge it will be for my friend to manage it physically, emotionally, and socially. I want to <u>complement him, when</u> he takes care of himself. I want him to be around for a long time.

1. affect on him
a. NO CHANGE
b. affect on him,
c. effect on him,

2. been increasing
a. NO CHANGE
b. has been increasing
c. has been increased

3. First diabetes
a. NO CHANGE
b. First of all diabetes
c. First, diabetes

4. or high blood sugar
a. NO CHANGE
b. , or high blood sugar
c. , or high blood sugar,

5. to hopefully fit
a. NO CHANGE
b. to fit
c. to hopeful fit

6. had all ready
a. NO CHANGE
b. have all ready
c. had already

6. complement him, when
a. NO CHANGE
b. complement him when
c. compliment him when

MISSION 4: Message Client Y about someone you know with diabetes or another chronic condition. Use at least one comma.

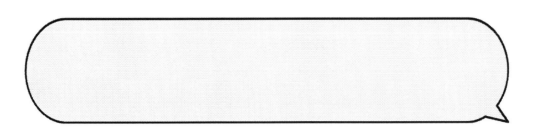

⚡ OPERATION 14: DASHES & PARENTHESES

The dash is a horizontal line used to separate groups of words, unlike the hyphen that is used to separate individual words. Two common dashes are the en dash and the em dash.

The en dash is shorter (like the size of an *N*). It is used to show a range.
I have read 15–20 pages.
This section has biographies from A–J.

The em dash is longer (like the size of an *M*). It is used to replace parentheses, colons, and missing information. The em dash can emphasize words and give writing a more casual feel.

I spend a lot of time in the library (usually in the mystery and biography sections).
I spend a lot of time in the library—usually in the mystery and biography sections.
I love two genres of books: mysteries and biographies.
I love two genres of books—mysteries and biographies.
I checked out a book with the faded title: *My——ery Island*.

Parentheses ( ) are used to enclose nonessential or extra information. Follow these rules for using parentheses.

1. Use a complete sentence or dependent clause if parentheses are not needed.
I rode my bike to the library (after I stopped at my friend's house). - incorrect
After I stopped at my friend's house, I rode my bike to the library. - correct

2. Use punctuation inside the parentheses if it is a complete sentence or requires different punctuation than the main sentence.
I heard my mother say she wanted me to mow the lawn (or did I?) before I left.
My mother asked me to mow the lawn before I left. (I wasn't sure I heard that.)

3. Use commas, colons, and semicolons outside the closing parenthesis.
When she asked me if I had mowed the lawn (louder this time), I had to admit I had not.

Write an example sentence for an en dash, em dash, and parentheses about the library or chores in the table below.

en dash
em dash
parentheses

CLIENT Z

MISSION 1: We asked Client Z to text you about her week. Add 13 DASHES and PARENTHESES and highlight them where they belong in the messages.

1. Well, my mom played pickleball the sport she wasn't interested in! with me.
2. It took her playing from 3:00 4:00 to get comfortable on the court.
3. There were three shots she loved lobs, smashes, and dinks.
4. After a warmup, she was trying to hit overhead smashes from the kitchen.
5. I had to explain multiple times! that kitchen shots can only be hit off the bounce.
6. I also had to repeatedly explain the scoring 0 0 2 to start the game.
7. The other thing I had to remind her 50 60 times, I think was not to hit a volley on the return of serve.
8. So, here's the funny thing she's playing more than I am now!
9. Some of the neighbors were playing and invited her to play in their league 2 3 days a week.
10. She's been playing so much that the J is worn off her paddle it reads OOLA now.

MISSION 2: Review the grammar graphics below. We will respond to your client with the text messages that follow. Add the correct word to the blank. Also choose from *all ready/already*.

Knew vs. New

I **knew** I should have set a reminder. But I'll know next time. (*past tense of know*)

Eew, I don't like the **new** soda flavor with cucumber. (*adjective*)

Compliment vs. Complement

GOOD JOB!

I gave him a **compliment** to praise him for a job well done.

We think you're the perfect **complement** to complete our team.

1. We _____ your mom would enjoy pickleball if she tried it!

2. And now she _____ has a league to play in.

3. What a _____ to be invited to play.

4. You introduced her to a _____ sport.

5. Will she be _____ to play doubles with you when you have time?

64

MISSION 3: Review your client's poster advertising a new pickleball league. Add any needed punctuation and highlight it. Also highlight any misspelled words.

KNEW PICKLEBALL LEAGUE FOR TEENS

New Century Park
12345 State Street
Canton Michigan

THURSDAY NIGHTS, 6:30 8:00

All skill levels beginner to advanced are welcome. After a brief lesson we'll match you with players to compliment your level of experience.

If you're ready for a little competition you are aren't you? join the league.

Please bring an outdoor ball pickleball paddle and bottled water and maybe a friend too! You'll be already to have fun. Note that adults aka parents have a league meeting Mondays and Wednesdays.

No need to RSVP. Just join us next Thursday night September 18th.

MISSION 4: Message Client Z about an activity your parents participate in. Use a dash or parentheses correctly.

OPERATION 15: ADVANCED QUOTATION MARKS

FAST FACTS

You've already learned these four quotation mark rules:

1a. Double quotation marks are used to indicate word-for-word verbal or written quotes.
He said, "I have to work, so I can't see the movie."
1b. Quotation marks are not used for paraphrases of what was said.

2a. Commas are used before or after the attribution of the quote (e.g., *said, reported, stated*).
"I can't see the movie this week," he told me.
2b. These commas are optional with one-word quotations.
2c. Quotations used as subjects or objects may not require a comma.
"Sorry I'm missing it" is what he wanted me to tell you.

3a. Complete quotes should be capitalized.
"I can't see the movie this week," he told me.
3b. Partial quotes that complete a sentence do not require capitalization.
He said he "can't see the movie this week," but he could go later.

4a. Double quotation marks can be used to indicate that a word is slang/jargon (used in a unique way by a particular group) or is ironic (opposite meaning).
He said he knew the movie would be "epic."
4b. Double quotation marks should not be used to emphasize a word as with bold type. Doing so risks miscommunicating irony.

Advanced Quotation Mark Rules

5. Put titles of short works like poems, chapters, and songs in quotes.
The only song I can play on piano is "Happy Birthday."

6. Put letters, words, or phrases in quotes to discuss them apart from their meaning.
The word "literally" doesn't mean what you think it means.

7. Use single quotation marks to indicate a quote within double quotation marks in American English. British English practice is the opposite.
The neighbor said, "The repair crew told me, 'It's the worst ice storm we've seen.'"

8. Use open quotes at the beginning of each paragraph of a multi-paragraph quotation. Put closing quotes only at the end of the final quoted paragraph.

9. Start a new paragraph every time the speaker changes.

Write an example sentence of a friend sharing a favorite song title within a quote. Use the American English form and put the song title in single quotes.

CLIENT Y

MISSION 1: We asked Client Y to text you about his week. Add 10 sets of QUOTATION MARKS where needed and highlight them.

1. Jack said he is feeling better since his diabetes diagnosis.
2. He said he's been singing James Brown's song I Feel Good a lot.
3. Even though he's feeling better, he said, I'm not sure about continuing in the business.
4. He said, My dad told me, Keep the main thing the main thing. But I don't know if our business is the main thing?
5. I said I thought main thing means his health.
6. He admitted that he isn't really feeling good.
7. It's been a lot harder to deal with than I thought, he said.
8. I said, Don't worry about the business right now. My song for you is You've Got a Friend in Me.
9. He said he appreciated my patience with him.
10. But I did remind him that the word Mensas in our business name means there is more than one genius at work.

MISSION 2: Review the grammar graphics below. We will respond to your client with the text messages that follow. Add the correct word to the blank. Also choose from *compliment/complement*.

Oversees vs. Overseas

The one who **oversees** the office keeps eyes on everyone. (*verb*)

We have **overseas** techs in Oceania. (*adjective; adverb*)

Knew vs. New

I **knew** I should have set a reminder. But I'll know next time. (*past tense of know*)

Eew, I don't like the **new** soda flavor with cucumber. (*adjective*)

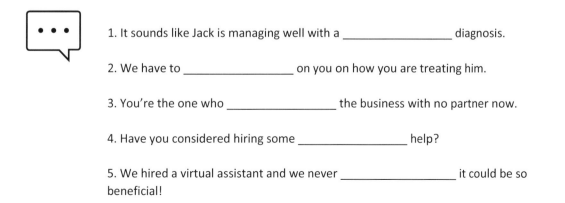

1. It sounds like Jack is managing well with a _____ diagnosis.

2. We have to _____ on you on how you are treating him.

3. You're the one who _____ the business with no partner now.

4. Have you considered hiring some _____ help?

5. We hired a virtual assistant and we never _____ it could be so beneficial!

MISSION 3: Review your client's ad for a virtual assistant. Highlight 14 errors. Note: Each comma and set of quotation marks is considered one error.

We are seeking a highly skilled oversees "virtual assistant" to remotely join our team. As a virtual assistant in a complimentary role, you will complete a variety of tasks in our social media business creating graphics scheduling posts, and updating our website.

The ideally candidate will have had excellent communication skills strong attention to detail, and the ability to work independently with minimal supervision. Candidates should all ready be fluent in English. Prior experience with Canva a graphic design program is a plus. Experience working with social media is preferred.

This is a remote position, requiring flexibility to have been working across different time zones. If you are motivated, hard-working, and eager to contribute to our team we would love to hear from you. To insure that you are considered for the position, please send us your resumé with "Virtual Assistant" in the subject line.

MISSION 4: Message Client Y how qualified you are for the position by quoting part of the ad.

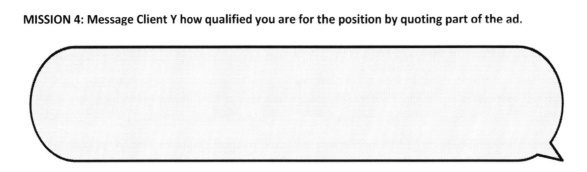

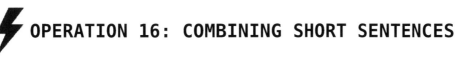 **OPERATION 16: COMBINING SHORT SENTENCES**

FAST FACTS

Writers combine short sentences to make their work less choppy and easier to read. There are three main ways of combining short sentences:

1. Create a compound sentence using a conjunction and a comma
I had a lot of homework. I didn't go to the movie.
I had a lot of homework, **so** I didn't go to the movie.

2. Create a compound subject or predicate
After dinner, I study. After dinner, I watch movies.
After dinner, I study and watch movies.

3. Insert an adjective or adverb
My friends don't want to hang out in the evenings. My friends are busy.
My **busy** friends don't want to hang out in the evenings.

For each type of sentence combining, write two short sentences and a combined sentence about busyness.

1.	
2.	
3.	

CLIENT Z

MISSION 1: We asked Client Z to text you about her week. Highlight 4 sets of consecutive messages that could easily be COMBINED INTO ONE SENTENCE.

1. I was so excited about the pickleball league.
2. I had talked to lots of friends about it.
3. I was sure they were coming.
4. But no one showed up!
5. My friend Becca said she had too much homework.
6. To my surprise, I got no response to my text messages from anyone else that night.
7. My friend Lily later admitted she was binge watching a show.
8. She's unreliable.
9. So I guess I'm not playing pickleball now.
10. My mom suggested I play in her league, but ugh.

MISSION 2: Review the grammar graphics below. We will respond to your client with the text messages that follow. Add the correct word to the blank. Also choose from *knew/new*.

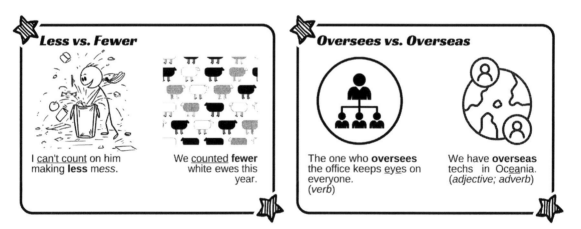

Less vs. Fewer

I can't count on him making **less** mess.

We counted **fewer** white ewes this year.

Oversees vs. Overseas

The one who **oversees** the office keeps eyes on everyone. (*verb*)

We have **overseas** techs in Oceania. (*adjective; adverb*)

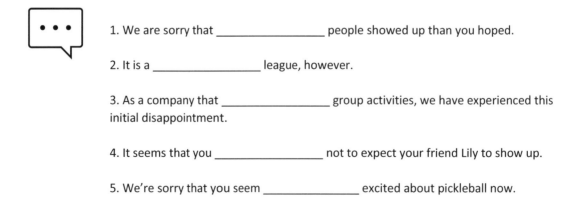

1. We are sorry that _____ people showed up than you hoped.

2. It is a _____ league, however.

3. As a company that _____ group activities, we have experienced this initial disappointment.

4. It seems that you _____ not to expect your friend Lily to show up.

5. We're sorry that you seem _____ excited about pickleball now.

MISSION 3: Review your client's essay. Highlight 2-3 sentences in each paragraph that could be combined. Write the new combined sentence in the space that follows.

I have been playing pickleball. I have been loving it. I thought starting a pickleball league for my friends was a fantastic idea. Several people said they'd heard of it and wanted to try it. I was sure that the league would be a success, but it was not.

I would not have been upset if a small group had joined the league. Instead, no one showed up to the first night. At first, I thought it was a bad night. And I should have sent a reminder. But then I realized that there was another reason: busyness.

Teens my age feel too busy. Between schoolwork, extracurricular activities, part-time jobs, and social obligations, the demands on their time seem never-ending. This busyness often leads to stress and lack of sleep. It leads to limited time for fun activities like pickleball.

While a certain level of activity is good for us, we need to find a balance. We have to use time management. We have to set realistic goals. And we need to get help making decisions. Then we might have time to join a pickleball league.

MISSION 4: Message Client Z what keeps you busy using a compound predicate.

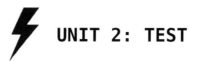 **UNIT 2: TEST**

Review the Fast Facts and grammar graphics sections of Operations 9-16. Then ask your trainer for the Unit 2 test. Record your score below.

Number correct out of 50_____ x 2 = _____ %

If you didn't score as well as you hoped, complete some review exercises you can find at FunToLearnBooks.com/FastGrammar2.

UNIT 3: ADVANCED PARTS OF SPEECH & AGREEMENT

OPERATION 17: ADVANCED PARTS OF A SENTENCE

FAST FACTS

Singular nouns mean only one person, place, or thing. **Plural** nouns are words that mean more than one of these.
1. Most nouns are made plural simply by adding –s. (kid, dollar, flower)
2. Some nouns become plural by adding –es. These are words that end in *ch, sh, x, s,* and sometimes *o*.
3. Irregular plurals are nouns that become plural in another way.
4. If you aren't sure of the plural form, see a dictionary for the abbreviation *pl.*

Linking verbs connect nouns or pronouns to a descriptive word (adjective) or explanatory noun (predicate nominative).
1. The most common linking verbs are forms of the verb **to be** (*am, is, are, was, were*). *Become* and *seem* are always linking verbs.
2. The verbs taste, smell, look, sound, feel, appear, turn, grow, prove, and remain can also function as linking verbs.

A direct object is a noun receiving the action of a transitive verb. To find the direct object, ask *what* after the verb. There are no direct objects with intransitive verbs. **An indirect object** is a noun or noun phrase affected by the action of a transitive verb but is not the main recipient of the action. Indirect objects usually come between the verb and the direct object. To find the indirect object, ask *who* or *what* got the direct object.

Subject pronouns take the place of subject nouns. These pronouns are said to be in nominative case. They often appear at the beginning of sentences. Subject pronouns do the action of a sentence or are what is being described. Subject pronouns are *I,* we, he, she, it, they, and you.
Object pronouns take the place of nouns acting as the direct object, indirect object, or object of the preposition (OP). These pronouns are said to be in objective case. They include *me, us, her, him, them, you,* and *it.* Object pronouns cannot be used as the subject of a sentence.
1. *You* and *it* may be used as both subjects and objects.
2. To remember which pronoun to use with compound subjects or objects (more than one), use only one pronoun. If it sounds wrong, try switching from object to subject or vice versa.
3. Use the pronoun *I* or *me* last in compound subjects and objects.

For each sentence part indicated, write an example sentence about the things that keep you busy.

irregular plural noun	
linking verb	
indirect object	
compound object pronoun	

CLIENT Y

MISSION 1: We asked Client Y to text you about his week. Highlight the SENTENCE PART indicated in brackets.

1. I haven't been able to find a VA who checks all the boxes. [plural noun]
2. One seemed talented but stopped responding to messages. [linking verb]
3. I asked every work candidate to give me a sample graphic. [indirect object]
4. Jack and I reviewed them. [subject pronoun]
5. Some candidates gave us the impression that their English wasn't good. [object pronoun]
6. Misspellings don't look professional, as you know. [linking verb]
7. We didn't discourage these candidates by mentioning the spelling. [direct object]
8. We may not be able to hire them, however. [object pronoun]
9. We will ask candidates to send additional samples to Jack and me. [object pronoun]
10. We may end up having to interview a whole new group of people. [irregular plural]

MISSION 2: Review the grammar graphics below. We will respond to your client with the text messages that follow. Add the correct word to the blank. Also choose from *oversees/overseas*.

Quite vs. Quiet

This wedding dress isn't **quite** it.
completely; fairly (adverb)

Baby Chet is usually **quiet**.
silent (adjective)

Less vs. Fewer

I can't count on him making **less** mess.

We counted **fewer** white ewes this year.

1. It sounds like your quest to find help has been _____ difficult.

2. We imagine that _____ international candidates are proficient in English.

3. Will you continue to consider _____ candidates?

4. Has Jack been _____ as he adjusts to his diagnosis?

5. We hope there has been _____ tension between the two of you.

MISSION 3: Review your client's essay on how to hire a VA. Highlight the corrections to be made on the right.

<u>My friend and me</u> want to hire a virtual assistant. I've learned that it's ₁ important to follow these steps to find the right candidate. First, define the specific tasks and <u>responsibilitys</u> you want your virtual assistant to handle. ₂ Then, thoroughly research and vet potential candidates. You don't want to roll a <u>dice</u> to choose someone! Consider their experience, skills, and ₃ communication style. Conduct interviews or trials to assess their compatibility with your working style. Does the applicant <u>seem quite</u>? Do ₄ they complete the assignment quickly and correctly? We asked several applicants to create graphics for <u>Jack and I</u>. Check references and reviews ₅ to make sure they are reliable and trustworthy. Clearly communicate expectations, deadlines, and payment terms upfront. Finally, establish a system for ongoing communication and feedback. That's what we plan to do when we find the right virtual assistant <u>for us</u>. ₆	1. A. NO CHANGE
	    B. Me and my friend
	    C. My friend and I
	    D. Him and I
	
	2. A. NO CHANGE
	    B. responsibilities
	    C. responsibility's
	    D. responsibilite's
	3. A. NO CHANGE
	    B. dies
	    C. die
	    D. die's
	
	4. A. NO CHANGE
	    B. seem quietly
	    C. seems quite
	    D. seem quiet
	
	5. A. NO CHANGE
	    B. Jack and me
	    C. we two
	    D. him and I
	
	6. A. NO CHANGE
	    B. for we
	    C. for he and me
	    D. for Jack and I

MISSION 4: Message Client Y what you would have a virtual assistant do if you had one. Use an object pronoun correctly.

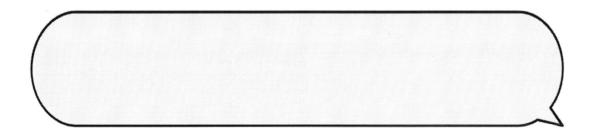

76

OPERATION 18: PROBLEMATIC SUBJECT/ VERB AGREEMENT

FAST FACTS

For subjects and verbs to agree in a sentence, both must be singular or both plural. Most singular verbs end in *s*. The verb *is* is singular and the verb *are* is plural. We have covered the following guidelines to make subjects and verbs agree:

1. Sentences that begin with the word <u>there</u>, <u>here</u>, or <u>where</u> use the verb <u>is</u> with a singular subject that follows and <u>are</u> with a plural subject that follows.
2. The contraction <u>doesn't</u> stands for <u>does not</u>. <u>Does</u> is a singular verb. The contraction <u>don't</u> stands for <u>do not</u>. <u>Do</u> is a plural verb.
3. Compound subjects (two or more nouns or pronouns connected by the word <u>and)</u> use a plural verb.
4. Singular nouns or pronouns connected by <u>or</u> or <u>nor</u> use a singular verb.
5. Compound singular/plural subjects joined by <u>or</u> or <u>nor use verbs that</u> agree with the subject closest to the verb.
6. Phrases between the subject and verb do not affect agreement of subject and verb.
7. Some subjects end in s (e.g., mathematics, civics, mumps) but require a singular verb.
The news is on.
8. Dollars may be singular or plural.
9. Nouns like *scissors*, *trousers*, and *shears* that have two parts are plural.
10. Collective nouns like *team*, *family*, *class*, and *management* are singular, but plural teams' names use a plural verb.

Review these additional guidelines to make subjects and verbs agree:

11. When subjects follow the verbs as in questions, ensure agreement.
How <u>are</u> Bob and Joan?

12. Collective nouns, nouns of amount, titles of books, and organization or country names are singular unless the individual members are being considered.
Number the Stars <u>is</u> a great book.

13. Avoid using subjects and predicate nominatives (joined by a linking verb) that differ in number, but match the verb to the subject.
The dessert and coffee <u>were</u> the last course served.

14. The words *every* or *many a/an* before a word or phrase takes a singular verb.
Every paint, marker, and chalk <u>is</u> used in art class.

15. Verbs in clauses followed by *one of those* are usually plural.
Ms. White is one of those teachers who <u>are</u> beloved by students.

16. The word *number* is singular when preceded by *the*. It is plural when preceded by *a*.
The number of students in art class <u>is</u> much higher this year.

Write an additional example sentence for guidelines 11-16 in the spaces above.

CLIENT Z

MISSION 1: We asked Client Z to text you about her week. Highlight 6 INCORRECT VERB FORMS in the messages.

1. My driver's license or job applications is on my mind right now.
2. The test on laws and punishments was easy.
3. But the number of things the driving evaluator will check worry me.
4. I could get one of those evaluators who marks everything wrong.
5. Many a student have failed the test the first time.
6. The written test and the driving eval is the last step before I get my license.
7. The Driving Association of the Americas is the sponsor of the driver's ed course I took.
8. The number of hours of driving experience required before testing are 40 in my state.
9. There are only two places to go for the driving test.
10. Once I pass, I hope the Bears hire me as a ticket agent!

MISSION 2: Review the grammar graphics below. We will respond to your client with the text messages that follow. Add the correct word to the blank. Also choose from *less/fewer*.

Formerly vs. Formally

I was **formerly** unhappy. (before)

We have not been **formally** introduced. (officially)

Quite vs. Quiet

This wedding dress isn't **quite** it. *completely; fairly* (adverb)

Baby Chet is usually **quiet**. *silent* (adjective)

1. If you pass your driving test, you'll _____ be a driver!

2. That's exciting and _____ a milestone.

3. We won't say who, but one of us took the driver's test no _____ than four times before passing.

4. If that makes you nervous, we'll be _____.

5. One of our staff members was _____ a ticket agent for a sports team.

MISSION 3: Review your client's description of the driving age debate. Highlight the corrections that should be made.

The debate surrounding teen <u>drivers revolve</u> around the question of
 ₁
 	
 what age young drivers like me should be allowed to get a license. The
 	
 argument for raising the driving age for teen <u>drivers is</u> that it would reduce
 ₂
 	
 accidents involving inexperienced drivers. Brain development <u>or maturity</u>
 ₃
 	
 <u>play</u> a crucial role in responsible driving. On the other hand, many <u>an</u>
 	
 <u>opponent argue</u> that the driving age should remain as it has been <u>formally</u>.
 ₄ ₅
 A license, they say, offers freedom and independence to teens and
 	
 prepares them for adulthood. They emphasize the need for good driver
 	
 education. The driving age debate is <u>one of those issues that are</u> likely to
 ₆
 	
 continue, while I hope to get my license soon!
	1. A. NO CHANGE
	    B. driver's revolve
	    C. drivers revolves
	    D. driver revolves
	
	 2. A. NO CHANGE
	    B. drivers are
	    C. driver's is
	    D. drivers' are
	
	 3. A. NO CHANGE
	    B. or maturity plays
	    C. and maturity play
	    D. either B or C
	
	 4. A. NO CHANGE
	    B. a opponent argues
	    C. a opponent argue
	    D. an opponent
	      argues
	
	 5. A. NO CHANGE
	    B. formerly
	    C. formal
	    D. former
	
	 6. A. NO CHANGE
	    B. one of those...is
	    C. one of this...are
	    D. one of these...is

MISSION 4: Message Client Z about your opinion on the driving age. Use guideline 14.

OPERATION 19: REFLEXIVE & INTENSIVE PRONOUNS

FAST FACTS

Reflexive pronouns are pronouns that end in *-self* or *-selves*. Reflexive pronouns include *myself*, oneself, ourselves, yourself, yourselves, himself, herself, itself, and themselves. Note that *theirselves* is not a reflexive pronoun. Reflexive is Latin for reflect. Reflexive pronouns are direct and indirect objects that reflect back to the subject of the sentence or clause.

I accidentally cut *myself* with a knife. – direct object
I gave *myself* a haircut. – indirect object

Intensive pronouns are reflexive pronouns that are not essential to the sentence but used for emphasis. They often directly follow their antecedent but can appear later in the sentence.

I *myself* am not a carpenter.
I am not a carpenter *myself*.
I am not a carpenter. – sentence without the pronoun

Reflexive pronouns cannot serve as subjects. A common error is to include a reflexive pronoun in a compound subject. To detect the error, remove the other subject from the sentence.

Joe and myself are going fishing this weekend – incorrect
Myself is going fishing this weekend. – subject removed, incorrect
Joe and I are going fishing this weekend – correct

Another common error is to use a reflexive pronoun as an indirect object that does not match the subject.

You can give Jane and *myself* the money later. – incorrect
(*myself* doesn't match the subject *you*)
You can give Jane and me the money later. – correct

Reflexive pronouns can serve as objects of prepositions if they match the subject, unless the preposition means "place" or "accompanied by."

They had to cook *for themselves*. – correct
She had the salt ready *beside herself*. – incorrect
He had his sister cooking *with himself*. – incorrect

Correctly use the word *myself* in new sentences as a direct object and an indirect object in the spaces below.

direct object	
indirect object	

CLIENT Y

MISSION 1: We asked Client Y to text you about his week. Highlight 4 INCORRECT REFLEXIVE/INTENSIVE PRONOUNS.

1. I haven't had any luck finding a VA by myself.
2. I gave myself a deadline of two weeks and that has passed.
3. Jack and myself started this business ourselves.
4. I thought I would always have him alongside myself.
5. I told Jack I was having trouble, and he said he would try to find help himself.
6. While he does that, I'm taking it upon myself to find another solution.
7. I'm testing artificial intelligence for tasks you don't have to do oneself.
8. AI can accomplish many tasks itself that I was doing.
9. For example, I am asking it to find business owners who aren't doing social media theirselves.
10. AI can even write introduction emails to them by itself!

MISSION 2: Review the grammar graphics below. We will respond to your client with the text messages that follow. Add the correct word to the blank. Also choose from *quite/quiet*.

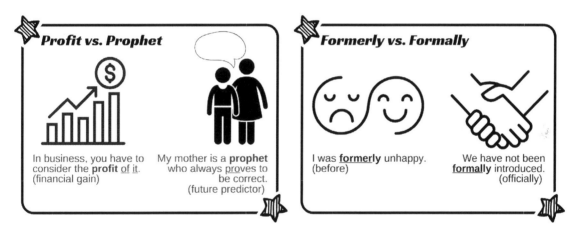

Profit vs. Prophet

In business, you have to consider the **profit** of it. (financial gain)

My mother is a **prophet** who always proves to be correct. (future predictor)

Formerly vs. Formally

I was **formerly** unhappy. (before)

We have not been **formally** introduced. (officially)

1. Using AI in your business could increase your _____s.

2. You don't have to be a _____ to think that AI will be managing many of our tasks in the future.

3. Things that _____ took us hours AI can do in minutes.

4. Have you _____ given up on your search for a VA then?

5. Has Jack gotten back to you, or has he continued to be _____?

MISSION 3: Review your client's meme and post about AI's role in managing social media. Highlight 11 errors.

My business partner and me have had no luck finding a VA. We want to save ourselves time without giving up prophets. Then I read that artificial Intelligence AI can complete some tasks formally performed by virtual assistants (VAs). As an example, AI made this meme for my partner and myself. The only thing I had to do myself was enter the text! AI assistants for various social media is able to determine the best time to post and then schedule those posts. AI chatbots can answer client questions and respond to messages for yourself, too, reducing the amount of time you have to spend online. A AI assistant can save oneself time and money. However, human VAs' creativity, empathy, and sense of humor are difficult for AI to copy. That's why business owners like us may want to do theirselves a favor and have a VA as well as an AI assistant.

MISSION 4: Message Client Y about your experience with AI. Use a reflexive or intensive pronoun.

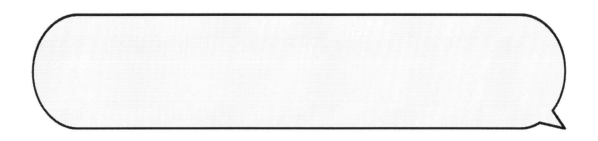

OPERATION 20: INDEFINITE PRONOUNS

Indefinite pronouns are pronouns that do not refer to specific nouns. To have subject-verb agreement with indefinite pronouns, learn which pronouns are singular and which are plural.

Always singular indefinite pronouns
pronouns ending in *-one*, *-body*, and *-thing*
another, each, either, much, little, neither, other

Always plural indefinite pronouns
both, few, many, others, several

Other indefinite pronouns are singular or plural depending on how they are used.
They include *all*, *any*, *more*, *most*, and *some*.
When used with a noun that can be counted, use a plural verb.
Some of the quarters are on the floor. (quarters can be counted; plural)
When used with a noun that cannot be counted, use a singular verb.
Some of the flour is on the floor. (flour can't be counted; singular)

When used to describe a noun (rather than standing alone), the words *any, each, few, some, many, much,* and *most* are indefinite adjectives. Verb agreement is with the noun.
Any player who breaks the rules will be eliminated. (singular verb)
Some kids prefer to work alone. (plural verb)

Write an example sentence for always singular and always plural indefinite pronouns. Then turn the page to review the examples.

always singular	
always plural	

Review the examples below. Then write an example sentence for an indefinite pronoun that is plural because it can be counted and an example sentence with an indefinite adjective.

Always singular indefinite pronouns
pronouns ending in *-one*, *-body*, and *-thing*
another, each, either, much, little, neither, other

Someone is in my seat! (singular verb)
Everybody has a place at the table. (singular verb)
Everything is beautiful! (singular verb)
Either is fine. (singular verb)
Much has been said about the topic. (singular verb)

Always plural indefinite pronouns
both, few, many, others, several

Few are able to pass the test. (plural verb)
Several have told me about the park. (plural verb)

Other indefinite pronouns are singular or plural depending on how they are used.
They include *all, any, more, most,* and *some.*
When used with a noun that can be counted, use a plural verb.
Some of the quarters are on the floor. (quarters can be counted; plural)
When used with a noun that cannot be counted, use a singular verb.
Some of the flour is on the floor. (flour can't be counted; singular)

When used to describe a noun (rather than standing alone), the words *any, each, few, some, many, much,* and *most* are indefinite adjectives. Verb agreement is with the noun.
Any player who breaks the rules will be eliminated. (singular verb)
Some kids prefer to work alone. (plural verb)

plural, counted indefinite pronoun	
Indefinite adjective	

CLIENT Z

MISSION 1: We asked Client Z to text you about her week. Highlight 4 INDEFINITE PRONOUNS/ADJECTIVES THAT DON'T AGREE WITH THEIR VERB.

1. I took my driver's test where everyone fails.
2. At least, few of my friends has passed.
3. Neither of my older cousins was able to pass their test there.
4. If most are failing their test, shouldn't they get a new evaluator?
5. Any driver feel nervous when being rated on their driving.
6. Some of the drivers who failed are afraid to go back!
7. In that case, something tell me it's not the drivers' fault.
8. I came to a fork in the road where the evaluator said, "Either are fine."
9. I went the wrong direction down a one-way street as many have.
10. But no one is happier than I am to report that I passed the test anyway!

MISSION 2: Review the grammar graphics below. We will respond to your client with the text messages that follow. Add the correct word to the blank. Also choose from *formerly/formally*.

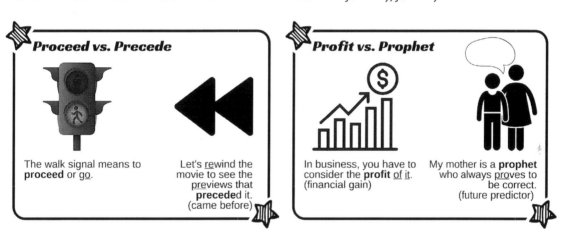

Proceed vs. Precede

The walk signal means to **proceed** or go.

Let's rewind the movie to see the previews that **preceded** it. (came before)

Profit vs. Prophet

In business, you have to consider the **profit** of it. (financial gain)

My mother is a **prophet** who always proves to be correct. (future predictor)

1. Congratulations! Now you are ready to _____ with your job application.

2. We're surprised that going the wrong way is what _____d you passing your test.

3. In this case, your friends and family weren't good _____s.

4. You are _____ a licensed driver.

5. Now you can _____ from having a job.

MISSION 3: Review your client's article on the benefits of teens having jobs. <mark>Highlight</mark> 10 errors.

I just got my driver's license and I'm ready to apply for my first job. There are less teens working than in past decades, but the rate is increasing. Some of the reasons for the lower rate is the economy, the requirement for volunteer hours for scholarships, and the internships that are unpaid and not included in employment statistics.

Experts agree that working too many hours while going to school can proceed negative affects of teen employment such as lower grades. However, there are numerous benefits to be gained. First, a job provides an opportunity for teens like me to gain valuable experience. A few of the things we can learn is responsibility, time management, teamwork, and problem-solving. Jobs also teach financial literacy, as we learn the value of money and how to budget. In addition, employment fosters independence and self-confidence. Some jobs helps us explore possible career paths and discover our interests. Finally, employment can give us a strong work ethic, discipline, and a sense of accomplishment. Overall, teen employment offers invaluable life lessons. It can set ourselves up for future success personally and professionally.

Most teens works in food service. I am hoping to get a job as a ticket agent. Anyone who have an "in" with the Bears should contact myself.

MISSION 4: Message Client Z about your job interest or experience. Use an indefinite pronoun or adjective.

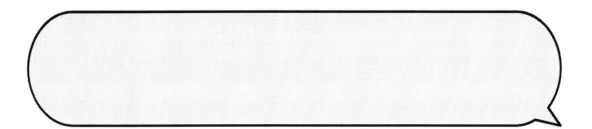

OPERATION 21: PRONOUNS, SPECIAL CASES

FAST FACTS

Pronouns in appositives are in the same case (subject or object) as the noun in apposition.
The two students, her and Grace, attended the meeting. – incorrect

The director gave the two students, she and Grace, free tickets to the concert. – incorrect

Use a possessive pronoun before gerunds (noun participles) in formal writing. Use a pronoun in object case or rewrite the sentence for informal writing.
Other students didn't object to his gifting of the tickets. – formal
Other students didn't object to him gifting the tickets. – informal

Use the pronoun that would be correct if the sentence were complete after *than* or *as*.
We wanted to attend the concert more than them [wanted to]. – incorrect

Rewrite the incorrect sentences correctly in the spaces above.

CLIENT Y

MISSION 1: We asked Client Y to text you about his week. Highlight 6 INCORRECT PRONOUNS in these informal messages.

1. Well, the two partners, Jack and me, are back in business!
2. I told him what I learned about AI.
3. I explained that it could be better than him!
4. That was my joking at his expense.
5. I said I needed a new partner, a VA, AI, or he.
6. I had him watching some videos on what AI can do.
7. He gave himself and myself a deadline for making a decision.
8. He knew I was less interested in hiring a VA than he.
9. After his review of AI possibilities, he is ready to get back to work.
10. The three of us, AI, Jack, and myself, are a team.

MISSION 2: Review the grammar graphics below. We will respond to your client with the text messages that follow. Add the correct word to the blank. Also choose from *profit/prophet*.

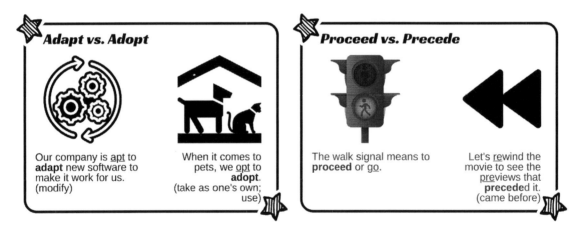

Adapt vs. Adopt

Our company is <u>apt</u> to **adapt** new software to make it work for us. (modify)

When it comes to pets, we <u>opt</u> to **adopt**. (take as one's own; use)

Proceed vs. Precede

The walk signal means to **proceed** or <u>go</u>.

Let's <u>rewind</u> the movie to see the <u>previews</u> that **preceded** it. (came before)

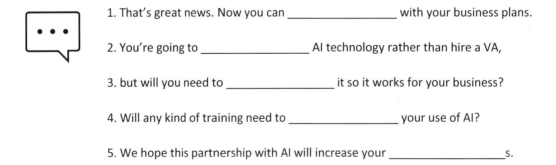

1. That's great news. Now you can _____ with your business plans.

2. You're going to _____ AI technology rather than hire a VA,

3. but will you need to _____ it so it works for your business?

4. Will any kind of training need to _____ your use of AI?

5. We hope this partnership with AI will increase your _____s.

MISSION 3: Your client asked AI to write copy for their marketing business. We asked AI to add 11 grammar errors for you to find. Please highlight them.

Introducing Marketing Mensas, the innovative social media marketing business powered by the brilliance of two teens, Jack and I. With their fresh perspective, digital savvy, and passion for social media, we are redefining the marketing game.

Marketing Mensa's combines cutting-edge strategies with a deep understanding of social media platforms to boost your prophets like never before. Harnessing our youthful creativity and tech-savviness, Jack and myself develop ingenious content strategies, captivating campaigns, and engaging visuals that resonate with your target audience.

Marketing Mensas specializes in skyrocketing brand visibility, driving organic growth, and maximizing conversions. We not only adapt the latest trends, we adopt them to make them work in your business. With regards to our competitors, we will deliver better results than them—guaranteed!

With Marketing Mensas, you gain the advantage of young minds with a pulse on the digital world, including how to take advantage of AI. Our fresh ideas and out-of-the-box thinking will make your brand as competitive as it.

Ready to precede and level up your social media presence? Let Marketing Mensas, Jack and me, take your business to new heights! Contact us today for a consultation and get ready to witness the power of youthful brilliance.

MISSION 4: Message Client Y what you think of this copy. Use a correct pronoun after the word *than*.

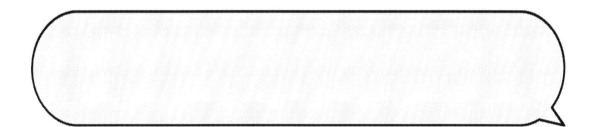

OPERATION 22: AMBIGUOUS PRONOUN REFERENCE

A pronouns' antecedent (noun that comes before and is replaced by a pronoun) should be clear. To make sure the pronoun is correct, substitute the antecedent.

My brother loves cars. *It* is his main interest.
[Cars] is his main interest. – incorrect subject/verb agreement

Ambiguous reference is when a pronoun's antecedent is missing or could be multiple options.

My dad and brother love cars, so *he* bought an old car they could work on together.

To clarify the antecedent, rewrite the sentence:

My dad, who loves cars, bought a car that he and my brother could work on together.

Or restate the antecedent:

My dad and brother love cars, so my dad bought an old car they could work on together.

Rewrite each sentence so the antecedent is correct and clear in the space below it.

My mother and sister disagreed about her curfew, and she looked upset.
My mother takes good care of her golf clubs. It is her favorite sport.
Put the telescope to your eye and adjust it until it's clear.

CLIENT Z

MISSION 1: We asked Client Z to text you about her week. Highlight 8-9 PRONOUNS WITH AMBIGUOUS OR INCORRECT REFERENCES.

1. As you know, I got my license last week. It has been fantastic!
2. My dad and brother congratulated me, but I think he's jealous.
3. He told me that I would have my own car to drive.
4. But that we would have to split the insurance deductible.
5. I think they can be very expensive!
6. I may need to get a job to pay for it.
7. I asked my dad if my brother would have to pay half my share when he gets a license.
8. My dad said that he may pay half my share unless we get another car for him.
9. My brother thinks he should get a new car now.
10. Then my brother can have his old car.

MISSION 2: Review the grammar graphics below. We will respond to your client with the text messages that follow. Add the correct word to the blank. Also choose from *proceed/precede*.

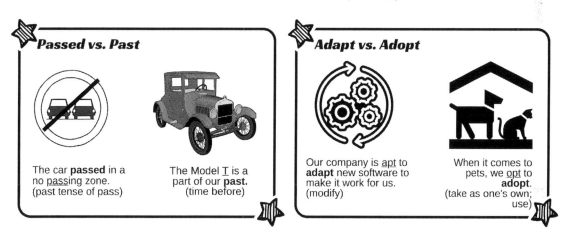

Passed vs. Past

The car **passed** in a no passing zone. (past tense of pass)

The Model T is a part of our **past.** (time before)

Adapt vs. Adopt

Our company is apt to **adapt** new software to make it work for us. (modify)

When it comes to pets, we opt to **adopt**. (take as one's own; use)

1. It's so exciting that you _____ your driving test.

2. Many families _____ rules for car usage that are

3. identical to their _____ experience as teens.

4. Other families _____ the rules because cars and insurance are so expensive now.

5. Let us know how you decide to _____.

MISSION 3: Review your client's list of pros and cons of teens paying for their own vehicle. Follow the directions in the right column.

I just got my driver's license, and my father has asked that I pay half the insurance deductible before driving his car. That got me wondering about the pros and cons of teens paying for their own vehicles. In the passed, most young people paid for their own cars. I know he did!	Highlight 3 pronouns with ambiguous antecedents.

Underline 4 incorrect verbs.

Circle 3 incorrectly spelled words. |

There is three benefits of a teen contributing to the purchase of their own vehicle: financial responsibility, ownership pride, and work ethic.

First, contributing instill a sense of financial responsibility and independence. They learn the value of money, budgeting, and the importance of making informed financial decisions.

Second, by purchasing their own vehicle, teens develops a sense of ownership pride and accountability. It is more likely to take better care of the vehicle, ensuring regular maintenance and responsible driving habits.

Third, paying for a vehicle require teens to work, save, and develop a strong work ethic. They learn the importance of setting goals, working hard, and delaying gratification, which can translate into other aspects of their lives.

But there are also some drawbacks of teens paying for their own vehicle: financial strain, insurance costs, and distractions.

First, purchasing a vehicle is a significant financial commitment, and it may place a burden on teens like me who are still studying or working part-time. They can divert funds from other essential needs, such as education or savings.

Second, insurance premiums for teenage drivers are typically high due to their lack of experience. Teens may struggle to afford these premiums on top of other expenses, making car ownership financially challenging.

Finally, owning a vehicle can introduce distractions and shift priorities for teens. They may become more focused on their car and social activities, which can precede declines in academic performance and other responsibilities.

Ultimately, assessing individual circumstances, finances, and parents' guidance will proceed the decision to have a teen pay for a vehicle or not. My dad thinks having me pay half the insurance deductible is a good compromise.

MISSION 4: Message Client Z about your family's approach to car ownership for teens. Use a pronoun with a clear antecedent.

OPERATION 23: COMMONLY MISSPELLED WORDS

There are at least three ways that may help you to remember the spellings of commonly misspelled words.

First, consider the prefix, root word, and suffix of the word. For example, the word *unfortunately* is made up of the prefix *un-*, the suffixes *–ate* and *–ly*, and the root word *fortune*. When you know the rules for adding suffixes, you can put the word parts together correctly. The *e* in the root word *fortune* is dropped before adding the suffix *-ate*. This is because the suffix begins with a vowel. For the same reason, the word *coming* does not have an *e* because we usually drop it before adding *–ing*.

The second strategy is to look for words within the word. For example, the word *knowledge* has two words in it: *know* and *ledge*.

Third, make up a saying to help you remember a tricky spelling. The saying could be based on an acronym like "It's necessary to cut some services" to remember the spelling of *necessary*. The first letters of "cut some services" can remind you that there is one *c* and two *s*'s in the word. Or memorize a saying like "There are two *m*'s, two *t*'s, and two *e*'s in committee." Use the same strategy for remembering several words with the same unique spelling. For example, remember "Her resistance to his appearance at the dance." All three main words end in *-ance*. Combine the second strategy with the third to remember how to spell *finally*. "Fin finally became my ally."

For three of the words below that you misspell, write a way to remember the correct spelling in the chart on the next page.

accommodate	achieve	across	aggressive	apparently
appearance	argument	assassination	basically	beginning
believe	bizarre	business	calendar	Caribbean
cemetery	colleague	coming	committee	completely
conscious	curiosity	definitely	dilemma	disappear
disappoint	ecstasy	embarrass	environment	existence
familiar	finally	fluorescent	foreign	foreseeable
forty	forward	friend	further	gist
glamorous	government	guard	happened	harass
honorary	idiosyncrasy	immediately	incidentally	independent
interrupt	irresistible	knowledge	liaison	lollipop
millennium	Neanderthal	necessary	noticeable	occasion
occurred	occurrence	pavilion	persistent	pharaoh
piece	politician	Portuguese	possession	preferred
propaganda	publicly	really	receive	referred
religious	remember	resistance	sense	separate
siege	successful	supersede	surprise	tattoo
tendency	therefore	threshold	tomorrow	tongue
truly	unforeseen	unfortunately	until	weird
wherever	which			

Word	Strategy for Spelling Correctly

CLIENT Y

MISSION 1: We asked Client Y to text you about his week. Highlight 18 MISSPELLED WORDS in the messages.

1. I truely think AI can make us more successfull.
2. The peice of copy I sent you is the jist of what it can help us acheive.
3. Basicly, AI automates the writing process, so we feel like Neandarthalls in comparison!
4. The knowlege it draws from is immediatly and publically available.
5. The new millenium of progress does not dissappoint!
6. Is good writing skill realy even necessarry now?
7. The time savings of using AI to write is iresistible!
8. No, AI can't copy the idiosyncrasies of an individual's style.
9. And goverment and politicians are worried about propoganda.
10. But I think we're on the threshhold of a great new era of progress.

MISSION 2: Review the grammar graphics below. We will respond to your client with the text messages that follow. Add the correct word to the blank. Also choose from *adapt/adopt*.

★ **Write vs. Right**

Be sure to **write** it down.
(jot) *verb*

The two men had a fight about who was **right**.
(correct) *adjective*

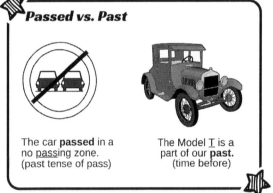

★ **Passed vs. Past**

The car **passed** in a no passing zone.
(past tense of pass)

The Model T is a part of our **past**.
(time before)

1. Even with AI, it's important to know how to _____ well.

2. It sounds like you think AI has _____ your test for a valuable tool.

3. Many people are _____ing AI as a business tool.

4. You may be _____ that this is the beginning of a new era.

5. But we believe that we will have to _____ AI's writing to make it more personal and effective.

MISSION 3: Review your client's AI-generated copy for a foreign-language learning company. Highlight 15 spelling errors we added.

Discover a World of Languages — Embrace the Multilingual Journey!

Are you tired of feeling limited when traveling or working across borders? Are you curious about different cultures and want to communicate effortlessly with people from various parts of the globe? Look no further. Our Foreign Language Course is here to help you achieve your language learning goals!

Embark on a Glamorus Adventure:

Step into a world of excitement as you begin your journey into the rich and diverse world of languages. We accommodate learners of all levels, from beginners to advanced, ensuring you find the perfect fit for your language learning needs.

Unlock New Opportunities Across the Globe:

Speaking a foreign language opens countless doors in business, government, and other sectors. Imagine impressing colleages and potential clients with your fluency in Portugese or navigating the Caribean with ease.

Beyond the Basics:

Our course goes beyond the basics. Delve deep into the peculiarities and idiosyncrisies of each language, gaining a deeper understanding of their culture and enviroment.

The Gist of Communication:

Master the essentials of communication — the vocabulary, grammer, and pronunciation — that will make you confident and irresistible in any conversation. No longer will you feel embarassed by language barriers.

Knowledge That Stands the Test of Time:

With our experienced instructors and proven teaching methods, you'll be well prepared for any forign language dilemma that may arise. You'll notice a significant improvement in your language skills as you progress through the course.

Surprizes Await You:

As you learn, you'll discover fascinating similarities and differences across languages, and occasionally, bazarre idioms that will keep you intrigued. With the global landscape changing rapidly, the ability to right and speak foreign languages is more necessary than ever. Be prepared for unforseen circumstances and grab opportunities wherever they may arise.

Join Our Multicultural Committee:

Our language-learning community is like a supportive commitee, encouraging you every step of the way. Forge connections with fellow learners from different backgrounds, fostering an environment of camaraderie and learning. Don't let language barriers hold you back; take the first step in your foreign language journey today! Remember, tomorrow's success is built on today's effort. Enrol now and embrace the extraordinary world of languages!

MISSION 4: Message Client Y about your experience with languages. Spell two commonly misspelled words correctly.

OPERATION 24: WRITING NUMBERS

Numbers should sometimes be spelled out and at other times should be left as numerals in writing.

WHEN TO SPELL OUT NUMBERS

- Numbers one to nine should be spelled out.

- Numbers at the beginning of a sentence should be spelled out or the sentence rearranged.

- When numbers appear next to each other in the text, one number should be spelled out.
He ordered *75 nine*-inch nails.
- In dialogue or quotes, numbers should generally be spelled out.

- When spelling out numbers, two-word numbers under 100 should be hyphenated.
"I counted out one hundred twenty-five buttons."

WHEN TO USE NUMERALS

- Use numerals for dates and numbers larger than nine.

- Use numerals for decimals. (Add a zero for decimals less than one.)
The chance of being struck by lightning in your lifetime is *0.0003* or 1 in 3000.
- Use numerals to stay consistent in describing something in a sentence, even if it breaks another rule.
She counted *5* of *20* pens that worked.
- Use numerals in science writing or directions.
Add *4* ounces of vinegar to *2 ½* tablespoons of baking soda.

WHEN TO USE BOTH SPELLING AND NUMERALS

- When writing about millions and billions, mix numerals and words.
Over *140 million* books have been published to date.
- When choosing whether to spell a number or use a numeral in writing, use a style guide. Or ask the teacher or publication you're writing for.

Write four example sentences in the spaces above where none is given. Then read the examples given on the next page.

Review the example sentences highlighted below. Then write a different example sentence in the spaces following the guideline.

WHEN TO SPELL OUT NUMBERS
- Numbers one to nine should be spelled out.
The girl grabbed *five* pencils.
- Numbers at the beginning of a sentence should be spelled out or the sentence rearranged.
Sixteen students enrolled in the class. The school enrolled *16* students.
- When numbers appear next to each other in the text, one number should be spelled out.

- In dialogue or quotes, numbers should generally be spelled out.
"I'm going to need *fifty* cupcakes."
- When spelling out numbers, two-word numbers under 100 should be hyphenated.

WHEN TO USE NUMERALS
- Use numerals for dates and numbers larger than nine.
By *1865*, more than *600,000* soldiers had died in the Civil War.
- Use numerals for decimals. (Add a zero for decimals less than one.)

- Use numerals to stay consistent in describing something in a sentence, even if it breaks another rule.

- Use numerals in science writing or directions.

WHEN TO USE BOTH SPELLING AND NUMERALS
- When writing about millions and billions, mix numerals and words.

CLIENT Z

MISSION 1: We asked Client Z to text you about her week. Highlight 7 NUMBERS THAT ARE WRITTEN INCORRECTLY.

1. $500 is the insurance deductible I have to pay.
2. That works out to me having to work forty hours to pay for insurance.
3. That's if I get a job making $15 an hour.
4. If I worked ten hours a week and 50 weeks a year,
5. that means I'd be spending .07 (7%) of my $7500 income on insurance.
6. That feels like seven million to me!
7. I'm not sure I want to work in fast food, measuring out ten cups of sugar for lemonade like my friend does.
8. I also have to pay for gas, which is $3 a gallon—
9. a lot more than the $1.19 my dad paid as a teen.
10. I'm thinking of trying to get proofreading jobs that pay three dollars a page.

MISSION 2: Review the grammar graphics below. We will respond to your client with the text messages that follow. Add the correct word to the blank. Also choose from *passed/past*.

Pour vs. Pore

Pour the <u>sour</u> lemon juice into the bowl. (spill)

He will **pore** over the book, looking for m<u>ore</u> information. (study)

Write vs. Right

Be sure to **write** <u>it</u> down. (jot) *verb*

The two men had a f<u>igh</u>t about who was **right**. (correct) *adjective*

1. So, you'd rather _____ over other people's papers

2. than _____ sugar into a batch of lemonade?

3. Proofreading others' work will help you _____ better.

4. It's amazing how inexpensive things were in the _____.

5. We didn't check your math, so we'll assume you're _____ about the percentage of your income you'll pay for insurance.

MISSION 3: Review the flyer Client Y made for Client Z. Highlight 14 number and spelling errors.

Are you tired of submitting documents with embarassing typos and grammer mistakes? Do you want your writing to leave a lasting impression on your readers? Look no further. My proofreading service is here to make your content shine!

Why Choose Me?
Attention to Detail: I pour over your content to insure that any errors disapear.

Wide Range of Content: I proofread academic papers, busyness reports, essays, and creative writing.

Fast Turnaround: I understand deadlines. Rest assured, you'll receive 1 to ten-page documents within forty-eight hours and longer documents within a week.

Confidentiality Guaranteed: Your documents are safe with me. I have submitted interesting stories to local papers, but I respect your privacy.

Affordable Rates: Quality proofreading doesn't have to break the bank. My rate is only three $ per page!

How It Works:
1. Email your document to me.
2. Recieve a quote based on the number of pages in your document.
3. Once payment is confirmed with a $.03 service fee per page, I get to work.
4. Your polished document will be sent back to you immediatly.

Let Your Words Make an Impact:
Students - Impress your professors with flawless assignments and boost your grades.
Professionals – Your writing will give you the appearence of authority.
Authors - Ensure your manuscript is ready for publication.
Righters - Let your creativity pore out while I take care of the details.

Contact me to discuss your project today!

MISSION 4: Message Client Z suggestions for improving her flyer, correctly writing a number.

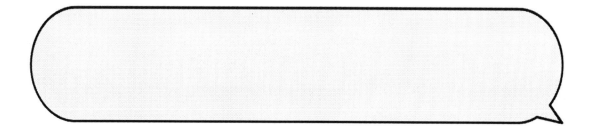

 **UNIT 3: TEST**

Review the Fast Facts and grammar graphic sections of Operations 17-24. Then ask your trainer for the Unit 3 test. Record your score below.

Number correct out of 50_____ x 2 = _____ %

If you didn't score as well as you hoped, complete some review exercises you can find at FunToLearnBooks.com/FastGrammar2.

UNIT 4: ADVANCED GRAMMAR & WRITING

⚡OPERATION 25: ADVANCED GRAMMAR & WRITING REVIEW

FAST FACTS

1. Participles are verb forms that can be used as part of a multi-word verb, as adjectives, or as nouns. Participles are present (end in -*ing*) or past (end in -*ed* for regular verbs) in form. Participles used as adjectives are known as verbals. Participles used as nouns are gerunds and always end in -*ing*.

2. A colon (:) is used to give more information (for lists of items or between independent clauses when the second explains the first). **A semicolon (;)** indicates a pause longer than a comma but shorter than a period (for lists of items that contain commas; between closely related sentences; and before the words *however*, *therefore*, and *for example* when they introduce independent clauses.

3. A run-on sentence is an incorrect grammatical structure in which two or more independent clauses are joined without one of the following: a period, semicolon (;), or comma and coordinating conjunction.

4. A misplaced modifier is words, phrases, or clauses separated from the word they explain, resulting in an uncertain meaning.

5. Parallel structure, also known as parallelism, requires using the same grammatical composition in a sentence.

6. Concise writing uses the fewest words needed to communicate effectively. To write concisely: replace several weak words with one stronger word; eliminate unnecessary introductions like *it is*, there is/are, I think/believe, and the fact of the matter is; and eliminate redundant words.

For each sentence below, write the number(s) of the concepts it's an example of.

Concept #	Example Sentence
	Skiing is a fun sport, they love going as often as possible.
	There are lots of things I'm bringing on the ski trip: goggles, helmet, gloves, coat, snow pants.
	At the thrift store, I found a blue man's hat, new ski gloves, and I found a ski mask.

CLIENT Y

MISSION 1: We asked Client Y to text you about his week. Highlight the CONCEPT INDICATED IN PARENTHESES for each message.

1. Writing with AI is much faster. [GERUND]
2. You enter a request you get the results. [WHERE A SEMICOLON SHOULD BE]
3. I don't know how it researches and writes so quickly, it's truly amazing. [WHERE A SEMICOLON SHOULD BE]
4. After using it many times, it's proven to be reliable. [MISPLACED MODIFIER CLAUSE]
5. I've used it to write social media posts, email, and I've used it to write video descriptions. [THE PART THAT ISN'T PARALLEL]
6. But the fact of the matter is, it's not perfect. [UNNECESSARY WORDS]
7. Some things I've noticed [WHERE A COLON SHOULD BE]
8. -using the same style of writing for every request [PARTICIPLE]
9. -repeated ideas throughout the writing [PARTICIPLES]
10. -its writing is not really new or interesting [WORDS THAT COULD BE REPLACED WITH ONE WORD]

MISSION 2: Review the grammar graphics below. We will respond to your client with the text messages that follow. Add the correct homophone to the blank. Also choose from *write/right*.

Forth vs. Fourth

We continued **forth** together, encouraged by our <u>forward</u> progress.

He was disappointed that with only <u>four</u> runners, he came in **fourth**.

Pour vs. Pore

Pour the <u>sour</u> lemon juice into the bowl. (spill)

He will **pore** over the book, looking for <u>more</u> information. (study)

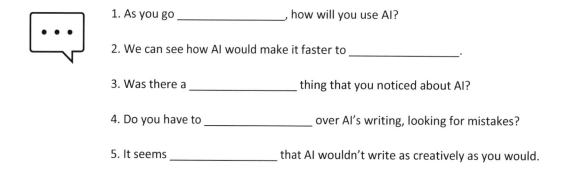

1. As you go _____, how will you use AI?

2. We can see how AI would make it faster to _____.

3. Was there a _____ thing that you noticed about AI?

4. Do you have to _____ over AI's writing, looking for mistakes?

5. It seems _____ that AI wouldn't write as creatively as you would.

MISSION 3: The client asked AI to write about its use in high school writing. We've added some errors. Highlight changes that should be made.

Using AI for high school writing assignments, <u>it can</u> learn a lot. AI-powered writing assistants can provide real-time <u>feedback: on</u> grammar, spelling, and <u>on sentence structure.</u> <u>With this feedback</u>, students improve their writing skills and self-editing abilities. Moreover, AI can assist in generating topic ideas, organizing content, and <u>source citations</u>, fostering critical thinking and research skills. It offers personalized learning opportunities, catering to individual student needs and <u>pacing. However,</u> it's essential to strike a balance, ensuring students still actively engage in the writing process and maintain their creativity. Teachers play a crucial role in guiding students on effectively utilizing AI tools while emphasizing the importance of originality and understanding the subject matter deeply.

1. it can
a. NO CHANGE
b. they can
c. students can

2. feedback: on
a. NO CHANGE
b. feedback on;
c. feedback on

3. on sentence structure
a. NO CHANGE
b. sentence structure
c. on structure

4. With this feedback,
a. NO CHANGE
b. delete
c. With student feedback,
d. With student feedback;

5. source citations
a. NO CHANGE
b. citing sources
c. sources

6. pacing. However,
a. NO CHANGE
b. pacing, however,
c. pacing: However

MISSION 4: Message Client Y your opinion of using AI for high school writing, using parallel structure.

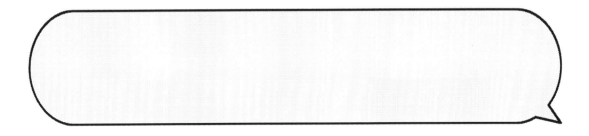

⚡ OPERATION 26: ACTIVE VS. PASSIVE VOICE

Passive voice is when the subject of a sentence is being acted upon. A sentence is in passive voice when a form of *be* (*is, am, are, was, were, being, been*) is paired with the past participle of the verb (i.e., the present or past perfect verb often ending in -ed).

The passive agent (that acts on the subject) may be added to the sentence with the word *by*.

The most books per capita are published in Britain.

Amazon self-publishers were paid half a billion dollars last year.

On average, more than 10 hours per week is spent reading by people in India.

Intransitive verbs that cannot have direct objects are never in passive voice (e.g., arrive, come, die, go, live, sleep).

Active voice emphasizes the subject as the acting agent.

Use passive voice sparingly (when you don't know the actor or don't want to disclose the actor). Active voice makes sentences easier to understand.

Rewrite the three *passive-voice sentences* into active voice in the space below each sentence.

CLIENT Z

MISSION 1: We asked Client Z to text you about her week. Highlight 6 messages in PASSIVE VOICE.

1. I received some responses from several people to my proofreading ad.
2. The first person wanted same-day service.
3. I didn't know that when I took the job.
4. I was told last minute!
5. After that, my terms of service were revised.
6. But then I had another problem.
7. The next client's paper was written so poorly
8. that I didn't know where to begin!
9. Papers that have been edited are what I need.
10. If I could get proofreading work from editors, that would be great!

MISSION 2: Review the grammar graphics below. We will respond to your client with the text messages that follow. Add the correct word to the blank. Also choose from *pour/pore*.

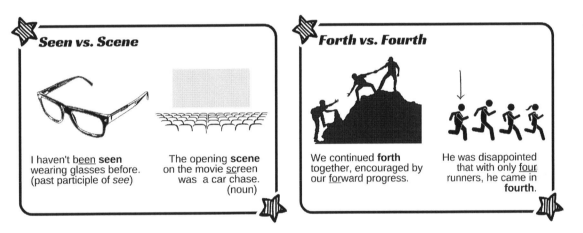

★ **Seen vs. Scene**

I haven't b<u>ee</u>n **seen** wearing glasses before. (past participle of *see*)

The opening **scene** on the movie <u>scr</u>een was a car chase. (noun)

★ **Forth vs. Fourth**

We continued **forth** together, encouraged by our <u>for</u>ward progress.

He was disappointed that with only <u>four</u> runners, he came in **fourth**.

1. We have _____ some poorly edited papers before, too.

2. You want to see that writers have put _____ some effort.

3. Are you proofreading nonfiction, or have you worked on any novel _____s?

4. Aspiring novelists _____ their heart and soul into the story.

5. But they also have to _____ over their writing in the editing process.

MISSION 3: Your client submitted one of her own client's romance-novel pages for your review. <mark>Highlight</mark> the best description for each underlined section.

In the quaint little town of Sweetville, <u>where love was rumored</u> to ¹ sprinkle like magic dust, stood two souls <u>destined to collide</u>. Amelia, a ² spirited florist with a heart as tender as the roses she tended, found herself swept off her feet by the <u>dashing newcomer, Gabriel</u>. With his mysterious past and captivating eyes that seemed to hold secrets, <u>it</u> was like a breath of fresh air in Amelia's world. As fate wove its enchanting web, their paths intertwined, and sparks flew amidst moonlit <u>seens</u>. With every soft touch and whispered word, their hearts danced to an enchanting rhythm, igniting a love that bloomed brighter than any bouquet Amelia ever crafted. In Sweetville's embrace, their love story unfolded, a sweet symphony of passion, hope, and the promise of a forever they <u>could of</u> only dreamed.

1. **where love was rumored**
   A. active voice
   B. passive voice
   C. undetermined voice
2. **destined to collide**
   A. active voice
   B. passive voice
   C. undetermined voice
3. **dashing...Gabriel**
   A. passive agent
   B. subject
   D. ambiguous reference
4. **it**
   A. ambiguous reference
   B. should be Gabriel
   C. both A & B
5. **seens**
   A. NO CHANGE
   B. scenes
   C. scene's
6. **could of**
   A. NO CHANGE
   B. could have
   C. couldn't have

MISSION 4: Message Client Z your opinion of this romance. Use the active voice.

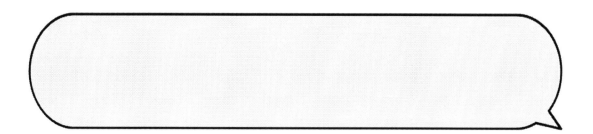

OPERATION 27: CONSISTENT SUBJECT/VERB FORMS

Shifts from one subject or verb to another within a sentence should be avoided unless necessary to the intended meaning.

Shifts in Subject

Students should proofread their papers, so you can be sure you won't lose points.

Shifts in Verb

Unnecessary shifts in subject are often related to a shift from active to passive voice.

She edited her paper, but no errors were found.

Shifts in verb tense should be avoided unless necessary.

The proofreader reviews the paper carefully and highlighted numerous errors.

To correct unnecessary shifts, omit the second subject and use a compound verb in the same tense.

Rewrite the italicized sentences in the space that follows them, using consistent subject and verb forms.

CLIENT Y

MISSION 1: We asked Client Y to text you about his week. Highlight 5 messages that include UNNECESSARY SHIFTS IN SUBJECT OR VERB.

1. I have been researching our business prospects and it's surprising.
2. AI is taking over and was the number one choice for companies' advertising.
3. Yes, we are being paid now, but will we be paid in the future?
4. Why should anyone pay when AI can do it for free?
5. I haven't told Jack yet, but the statistics had me worried.
6. More and more businesses are using AI for marketing.
7. Courses on how to use AI for marketing are big sellers.
8. Clients are looking for help, and these courses are being sold to them.
9. It seems like a very different business, but print-on-demand is an option for us.
10. Print-on-demand is excellent passive income, and AI made it happen.

MISSION 2: Review the grammar graphics below. We will respond to your client with the text messages that follow. Add the correct word to the blank. Also choose from *forth/fourth*.

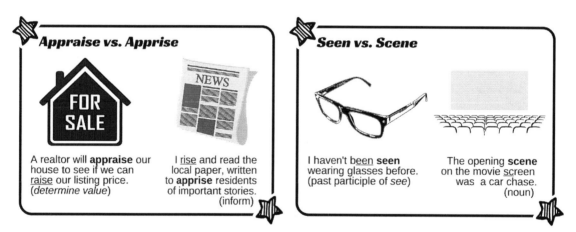

Appraise vs. Apprise

A realtor will **appraise** our house to see if we can raise our listing price. (*determine value*)

I rise and read the local paper, written to **apprise** residents of important stories. (*inform*)

Seen vs. Scene

I haven't been **seen** wearing glasses before. (past participle of *see*)

The opening **scene** on the movie screen was a car chase. (*noun*)

1. It's wise of you to _____ the value of your services in light of AI.

2. We have also _____ a lot of marketing AI courses.

3. An internet search of marketing services lists AI in the first through the _____ result.

4. Business changed when AI arrived on the _____.

5. When will you _____ your business partner of your research?

MISSION 3: Review the email your client wants to send to his business partner about print-on-demand business. Highlight changes that should be made.

Hey, Jack. I've been thinking about our business, and I <u>had wanted to appraise</u> you of my thoughts. <u>Business is being changed by AI</u>. We <u>have seen</u> the benefits of it. But I am concerned about the future. Why will a company pay us when AI is free? I listened to a podcast, and the benefits of a print-on-demand (POD) business <u>were explained</u>. POD businesses produce custom shirts, bags, and <u>produce custom gifts.</u> POD businesses <u>reduce the need for a large upfront investment in inventory, and operational costs are reduced.</u> The flexibility of POD enables quick adaptation to market trends. And AI can help us with every step of the business—from deciding what to sell to designing graphics. I'll send you a link to the podcast. Let me know your thoughts after you've listened.	**1. had wanted to appraise** a. NO CHANGE b. had wanted to apprise c. want to apprise **2. Business is…AI** a. NO CHANGE b. AI is changing business c. Business is changing AI **3. have seen** a. NO CHANGE b. had seen c. have scene **4. were explained** a. NO CHANGE b. delete c. rewrite sentence **5. produce custom gifts** a. NO CHANGE b. produce gifts c. gifts **6. reduce the need…** a. NO CHANGE b. reduce operational costs and the need for… c. reduces the need for…

MISSION 4: Message Client Y about a POD product you've purchased. Use a compound verb in consistent tense.

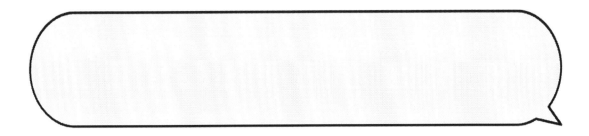

111

OPERATION 28: GRAMMATICAL MOOD

Grammatical mood is used to make the writer's or speaker's intention clear, primarily by the form and tone of the verb. There are five main types of grammatical mood.

1) Interrogative mood asks a question and uses helping verb forms of *be, do, is,* and *have.*
2) Imperative mood issues a command, often with the subject *you* understood but not specified.
3) Indicative mood makes statements of fact or belief.
4) Conditional mood is a statement that is dependent on conditions. It includes the helping verbs *would* and *should* and may use the if/then construction.
5) Subjunctive mood expresses a wish for something that may not be possible. The verb can indicate a desire, a suggestion, or a demand that may not be realized. The subjunctive uses the third-person (he, she, they) form of the verb without the *-s,* and it uses *be* rather than *is/are*. When describing a wish or a possibility, use *were* instead of *was.*

Write the number of the grammatical mood of each example sentence below.

Mood Number	Example Sentence
	If I were a millionaire, I'd buy a yacht.
	When we see the movie, we should get some popcorn.
	My mother worries about kids who ride bikes without helmets.
	Grab me a pencil, please.
	When will you have enough money?
	The teacher desires that students be heard.
	There are more than 3,000 billionaires in the world.
	Are you going to the game with us?
	If my friend decides not to go, then I wouldn't go.
	The coach suggested that the player seek a batting coach.

CLIENT Z

MISSION 1: We asked Client Z to text you about her week. Highlight 3 INCORRECT VERBS FOR THE SUBJUNCTIVE MOOD.

1. I told my romance-novel client what I thought of her book.
2. That was a big mistake!
3. She said if she'd wanted my opinion of the story, she would have asked.
4. She obviously wishes she was a best-selling novelist.
5. But she is just getting started.
6. She needs more than just proofreading, as you've seen.
7. I recommended that she finds a good editor.
8. She said her mom loves it and that's good enough for her.
9. Her next step is to find a literary agent.
10. If I was an agent, I would give her book a hard pass!

MISSION 2: Review the grammar graphics below. We will respond to your client with the text messages that follow. Add the correct word to the blank. Also choose from *seen/scene*.

Rain vs. Rein vs. Reign

Ray forecasts **rain**. (precip)

The cowboy uses the **rein** to **rein** in the rebellious horse. (strap/guide)

Queen Gina began her **reign** in the 1800s. (rule)

Appraise vs. Apprise

A realtor will **appraise** our house to see if we can raise our listing price. (*determine value*)

I rise and read the local paper, written to **apprise** residents of important stories. (inform)

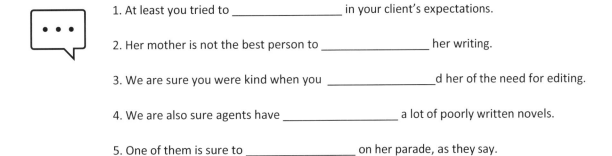

1. At least you tried to _____ in your client's expectations.

2. Her mother is not the best person to _____ her writing.

3. We are sure you were kind when you _____ d her of the need for editing.

4. We are also sure agents have _____ a lot of poorly written novels.

5. One of them is sure to _____ on her parade, as they say.

MISSION 3: Review the email your client is sending to the romance novelist. Highlight 8 sentences that have the WRONG VERB FORM FOR SUBJUNCTIVE MOOD, HAVE AN UNNECESSARY SHIFT IN SUBJECT OR VERB FORM, or are WRITTEN IN PASSIVE VOICE. <u>Underline</u> 3 incorrectly written words.

Subject: Honest Insights for Your Writing Journey

I hope you are not upset about the writing feedback I gave you. My desire is that my clients are happy with my work.

But I also want my clients to be realistic. You said your dream is to be a full-time romance novelist. I think it's wise to reign in your expectations.

The romance genre is popular with more than $one billion in sales, but you're in a highly competitive market. Succeeding will require exceptional storytelling. The market is saturated, making it difficult for you to gain a following. And over 99% of manuscripts are rejected by publishers.

I've already mentioned the benefits of professional editing. But you should also consider writing in different genres. Of course, the more you write, the more you'll improve. Once you have an excellent book, it wouldn't hurt to hire a social-media marketer like my brother. He can help you build a following that can lead to book sales. Let me know if you want his number.

If I was to guess, I don't see you succeeding as a romance novelist. But that doesn't mean you couldn't write nonfiction. Have you considered writing articles for the local paper? Perhaps you could write book reviews?

If you still desire to write, it is a good idea to remember the obstacles successful authors have faced. The journey must be pursued with dedication, despite its demands and uncertainties.

I know you didn't want me to appraise your content, but I want to be honest. I also know you want to put your best work fourth, or you wouldn't have asked me to proofread for you. I wish I was a writing fairy and could make your dream happen for you. But because I'm not, I hope this honest email is the next best thing.

All the best,

MISSION 4: Message Client Z what you think of this email, using the subjunctive mood correctly.

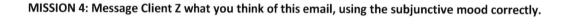

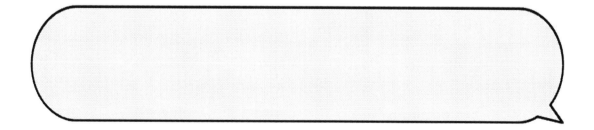

OPERATION 29: COMBINING SENTENCES WITH CLAUSES & PHRASES

Short, related sentences may be combined with adjective, adverb, or noun subordinate clauses.

To combine sentences using an adjective clause, choose the correct relative pronoun for the most important subject in the sentence.
The movie had a lot of violence.
I found it hard to watch.

Adverb clauses show the relationship between the combined sentences in terms of how, when, or why. Choose the subordinating conjunction which best indicates the relationship. To keep the emphasis on the main clause, consider opening the sentence with the subordinate clause.
I was looking forward to the movie.
I can't recommend it.

Noun clauses are used as subjects, predicate nominatives, and indirect objects in combined sentences. They often begin with *that, what, whatever, why, whether, how, who,* or *whoever.*
Can viewers stomach the blood and gore?
That is the deciding factor for seeing the film.

Short, related sentences can also be combined with prepositional, participial, or appositive phrases.

Use prepositional phrases in a way that preserves clarity and fluency.
The movie was playing in multiple theaters.
The movie was playing at multiple show times.

Participial phrases should be used adjacent to the nouns they describe.
The audience was screaming in fear.
They still seemed to be enjoying themselves.

Nonessential appositive phrases should be separated with commas when used to combine short sentences.
This movie is selling a record number of tickets.
It is a film in the horror genre.

In the spaces above, combine each set of sentences into a single sentence using the type of clause or phrase indicated.

CLIENT Y

MISSION 1: We asked Client Y to text you about his week. Highlight 3 SETS OF ADJACENT MESSAGES THAT COULD BE COMBINED WITH CLAUSES OR PHRASES.

1. After waiting, I haven't heard from Jack about my POD business idea.
2. It's been three days!
3. I don't even know if he listened to the podcast I sent him about POD business.
4. I had my dad listen to it, and he was impressed.
5. Should I start the business without him?
6. I don't know.
7. My dad did say I could have Shiny Object Syndrome.
8. That's the habit of pursuing the latest, exciting thing instead of staying focused.
9. There is a reason to continue with social-media marketing.
10. My sister says she can refer her proofreading clients to me, so that's something to consider.

MISSION 2: Review the grammar graphics below. We will respond to your client with the text messages that follow. Add the correct word to the blank. Also choose from *appraise/apprise*.

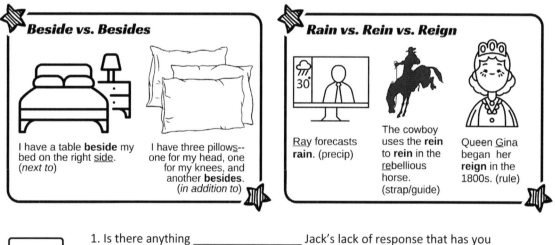

Beside vs. Besides

I have a table **beside** my bed on the right <u>side</u>. (*next to*)

I have three pillow<u>s</u>-- one for my head, one for my knees, and another **besides**. (*in addition to*)

Rain vs. Rein vs. Reign

<u>Ray</u> forecasts **rain**. (precip)

The cowboy uses the **rein** to **rein** in the <u>rebellious</u> horse. (strap/guide)

Queen <u>Gina</u> began her **reign** in the 1800s. (rule)

1. Is there anything _____ Jack's lack of response that has you reconsidering a POD business?

2. We are sure you would like to have him _____ you in a new business venture.

3. Did your father's mention of Shiny Object Syndrome _____ in your enthusiasm?

4. Be sure to _____ us what Jack says about your business idea.

5. Have you _____d the likelihood of your sister sending you paying clients?

MISSION 3: Review the email your client sent to his business partner. Highlight any ADJACENT SENTENCES THAT COULD BE COMBINED USING CLAUSES OR PHRASES. <u>Underline</u> any INCORRECT WORDS.

Hey, Jack.

I haven't heard back from you about the podcast. That podcast talks about POD business. I'm sure you've been busy. Although I was eager to hear from you, it may be for the best that you haven't responded.

I've been thinking about our goals and skill sets. I realized that I wasn't seeing all the possibilities. At first I wondered if I had Shiny Object Syndrome. That's the habit of shifting focus to something new and exciting. It will come as no surprise to you that I suffer from that syndrome. This time, however, I don't think that I should just forget it and move on.

We are a marketing business. We help business owners sell their products and services. But we have also struggled to find clients. What if we start a POD business and use our marketing skills to drive sales? That way we have real numbers to show Marketing Mensa clients! Of course, we would enjoy extra revenue beside.

My idea is to run both businesses. Let me know what you think of that. It would require putting fourth our best efforts. Do you have time to pore yourself into business right now?

I look forward to hearing from you.

MISSION 4: Message Client Y about his idea of running both businesses, using a clause.

⚡ OPERATION 30: SENTENCE VARIETY

Writers can avoid monotony in writing by varying sentence length and structure. Rather than beginning with an article adjective (*a, an, the*) or the subject of the sentence, writers can begin sentences with:

- **an adverb**

- **a prepositional phrase**

- **a participial phrase**

- **an appositive**

- **an infinitive phrase**

- **two adjectives**

- **transition words**

- **subordinating conjunctions**

Write an example sentence about running for each type of sentence starter above. Then review the examples on the next page.

Review the examples below. Then rewrite the sentences, starting with the subject.

- **an adverb** *Slowly,* the girl passed the runner ahead of her.

- **a prepositional phrase** *At the start of the race*, there was no lead runner.

- **a participial phrase** *Gasping for breath*, the miler crossed the finish line.

- **an appositive** *The 14th high school athlete to run a mile under 4 minutes*, Gary Martin set a new record in 2022.

- **an infinitive phrase** *To win the race*, the hurdler trained daily.

- **two adjectives** *Hot and tired*, the runner finished the marathon.

- **transition words** *Finally*, at the six-hour mark, the last runner crossed the finish line.

- **subordinating conjunctions** *Whether* it rains or not, we are running the race.

CLIENT Z

MISSION 1: We asked Client Z to text you about her week. Highlight THE SENTENCE STARTER THAT WOULD ADD VARIETY TO THE MESSAGES.

1. The romance novelist was angry and unappreciative and said she won't need my help again.
2. The woman, an aspiring novelist, doesn't know how to take constructive criticism.
3. She said harshly that she didn't need advice from a high school student.
4. She needs an editor to get published.
5. I don't regret what I wrote despite her response.
6. She is frustrated with herself and taking it out on me.
7. She hasn't written a best-selling romance whether she knows it or not.
8. I am tired and annoyed and not sure I want to keep proofreading.
9. I am rethinking it since working with her.
10. I have taken up running to relax.

MISSION 2: Review the grammar graphics below. We will respond to your client with the text messages that follow. Add the correct word to the blank. Also choose from *rain/rein/reign*.

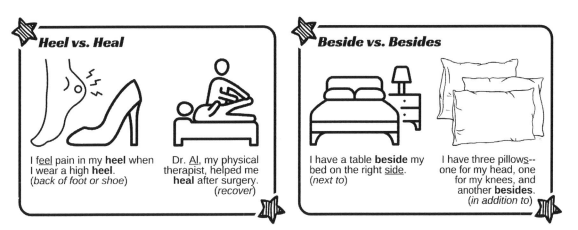

Heel vs. Heal

I f**ee**l pain in my **heel** when I wear a high **heel**. (*back of foot or shoe*)

Dr. A̲l, my physical therapist, helped me **heal** after surgery. (*recover*)

Beside vs. Besides

I have a table **beside** my bed on the right s̲i̲d̲e̲. (*next to*)

I have three pillow̲s-- one for my head, one for my knees, and another **besides**. (*in addition to*)

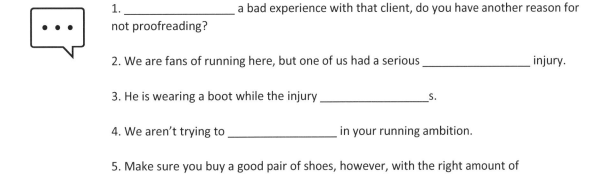

1. _____ a bad experience with that client, do you have another reason for not proofreading?

2. We are fans of running here, but one of us had a serious _____ injury.

3. He is wearing a boot while the injury _____s.

4. We aren't trying to _____ in your running ambition.

5. Make sure you buy a good pair of shoes, however, with the right amount of _____-to-toe drop (difference in height from back to front).

MISSION 3: Review your client's article for aspiring marathon runners. Rewrite the sentences that have a line space beneath them, using the sentence starter in brackets.

I have a few essential pieces of advice for you aspiring marathon runners. [prepositional phrase]

First, create a training plan that gradually increases mileage. Be sure to include rest days to prevent overuse injuries. Incorporate cross-training and strength exercises to build fitness and reduce injury. [participial phrase]

Proper nutrition and hydration are crucial. [transition word]

Fuel your body with balanced meals rich in carbohydrates, proteins, and healthy fats. Practice using energy gels or chews during long runs. Hydrate consistently to avoid dehydration. [infinitive phrase]

Third, invest in good running shoes. You are looking for supportive and cushioned shoes. [two adjectives]

Break the shoes in as soon as you buy a pair. [subordinate conjunction]

Listen to your body and don't ignore warning signs of injury. Prioritize sleep for optimal recovery and performance.
Mental preparation is the final step. [transition word]

You will cross the finish line triumphantly when you set realistic goals, visualize success, and cultivate a positive mindset. [adverb]

MISSION 4: Message Client Z about your interest in running a marathon. Choose one of the sentence starters you've learned.

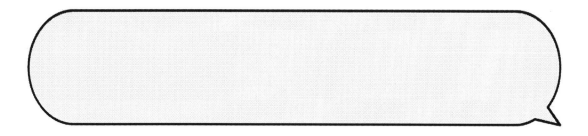

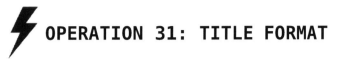

FAST FACTS

Titles of books, poems, movies, television shows, music albums, computer games, and other creative works must be set apart to prevent confusion. Capitalization sets titles apart. The two most common ways to capitalize titles are title case and sentence case.

In **title case**, the first, last, and major words (including proper nouns) of a sentence are capitalized. Article adjectives (*a, an, the*); coordinating conjunctions (*for, and, nor, but, yet, so*); and short prepositions of fewer than four letters (*by, in, of, on, out, to, up*) are not capitalized in title case. Short verbs (is, are, am) <u>are</u> capitalized in title case.

In **sentence case**, only the first word in a title and proper nouns are capitalized, just as in a sentence.

When choosing title capitalization rules, use the case required by a teacher or publication and be consistent.

Titles can also be <u>underlined</u>, *italicized*, or "put in quotations" to set them apart. Italic is a print type, first used by an Italian printer, that slants to the right and is used to separate information. The general rule is that the titles of complete works are underlined in a handwritten document and italicized in a typed document.

Parts of a larger work are set off by quotations.

Write an example title in title case and sentence case in the line spaces above. Also write a sentence with an underlined title. Finally, write a sentence with a song title in quotation marks and the album it appears in underlined. Both should be in title case.

CLIENT Y

MISSION 1: We asked Client Y to text you about his week. <u>Underline</u> TITLES or put them in quotation marks as needed. Highlight WORDS THAT SHOULD BE CAPITALIZED IN TITLE CASE.

1. You probably won't believe this, but Jack is starting a band called bacon bits.
2. He said he wrote a song called I made an omelet out of our breakup.
3. He already has an album name: riffs and recipes.
4. If it sells well, he'll publish a cookbook called culinary chemistry for teens.
5. He should really call his album shiny object syndrome.
6. It doesn't look like we'll be writing how to succeed in online business any time soon.
7. I think Jack is as good in the kitchen as Mike of the brady bunch.
8. In an episode called the grass is always greener, Mike has several kitchen accidents.
9. I know Jack is a fan of the TV show the monkees and would like to find three more band members.
10. He says he'll use his marketing mensas experience to market his music.

MISSION 2: Review the grammar graphics below. We will respond to your client with the text messages that follow. Add the correct word to the blank. Also choose from *beside*/besides.

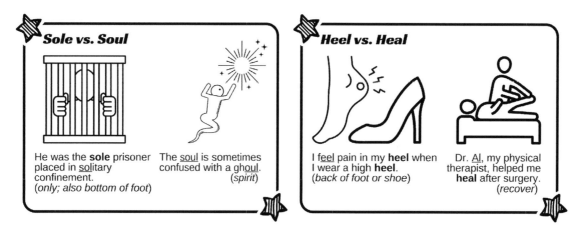

Sole vs. Soul

He was the **sole** prisoner placed in <u>solitary</u> confinement.
(*only; also bottom of foot*)

The <u>soul</u> is sometimes confused with a gh<u>oul</u>.
(*spirit*)

Heel vs. Heal

I f<u>eel</u> pain in my **heel** when I wear a high **heel**.
(*back of foot or shoe*)

Dr. <u>Al</u>, my physical therapist, helped me **heal** after surgery.
(*recover*)

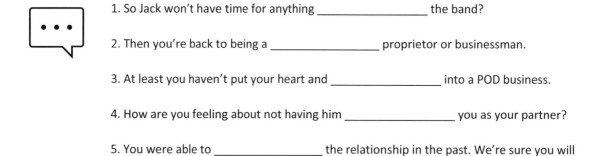

1. So Jack won't have time for anything _____ the band?

2. Then you're back to being a _____ proprietor or businessman.

3. At least you haven't put your heart and _____ into a POD business.

4. How are you feeling about not having him _____ you as your partner?

5. You were able to _____ the relationship in the past. We're sure you will again.

MISSION 3: Your client was asked to create an album cover for his friend Jack. Highlight every word that should be capitalized in title case.

tracks

1. "sizzling strings and savory spices"
2. "rock 'n' roll risotto"
3. "funky frittata"
4. "groovy grub"
5. "tunes and tacos"
6. "i have the bacon blues"
7. "melodies with my munchies"
8. "jammin' with muffins"
9. "chording in chocolate"
10. "i made an omelet out of our breakup"

riffs & recipes

MISSION 4: Message Client Y a song title Jack could add to his album. Use quotes and correct title case.

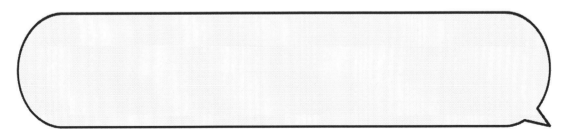

⚡ OPERATION 32: PROOFREADING

FAST FACTS

Using the following tips will help you catch more of your clients' grammar errors:
- Read the material aloud.
- Eliminate distractions as you proofread.
- Look for the most common mistakes listed below.

1. homophones (look for *to/too, there/their/they're,* and *your/you're* errors)
2. sentence fragments
3. run-on sentences with comma splices
4. verb tense errors
5. lack of agreement between subject and verb
6. incorrect pronoun
7. uncapitalized proper nouns
8. missing comma in a list or before a coordinating conjunction
9. missing or misplaced apostrophe
10. unnecessary shift in subject or verb tense

Write the number for the error in each sentence below.

Error Number	Sentence
	Kacy and myself are going to the concert together.
	We are using her dads tickets from work.
	She of all my friends are the most excited about this band.
	We're meeting some other friends their.
	I seen that the band was going to be here and told Kacy we should go.
	Because of their popularity.
	The concert sold out immediately, it's amazing we got tickets.
	I brought enough money to buy a shirt a drink and a snack.
	The concert is at the family arena.
	If we want to get home before midnight, you have to leave before the last song.

CLIENT Z

MISSION 1: We asked Client Z to text you about her week. Highlight ANY ERRORS in her messages.

1. Big news to share!
2. It's not about the marathon, that's still coming up.
3. I had take the college entrance exam, and I just got my scores back.
4. My science math and reading scores were okay.
5. But my English score was outstanding!
6. Whats even better is that I already got a letter from the American school of journalism.
7. They want me to apply for admission and a scholarship to!
8. It, of all the journalism schools, are my top choice.
9. You need a great English score to be accepted, and I'm grateful that I got one.
10. I want to thank you for the help you've given my brother and I.

MISSION 2: Review the grammar graphics below. We will respond to your client with the text messages that follow. Add the correct word to the blank. Also choose from *beside/besides*.

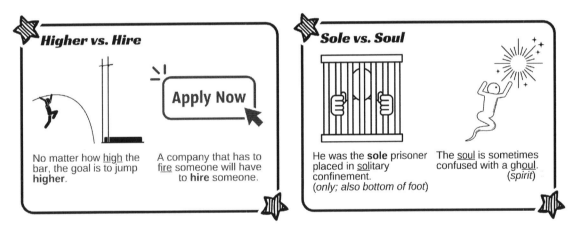

Higher vs. Hire

No matter how <u>high</u> the bar, the goal is to jump **higher**.

A company that has to <u>fire</u> someone will have to **hire** someone.

Sole vs. Soul

He was the **sole** prisoner placed in <u>sol</u>itary confinement.
(only; also bottom of foot)

The <u>soul</u> is sometimes confused with a gh<u>oul</u>.
(spirit)

1. You are _____ly responsible for this achievement!

2. You have poured your heart and _____ into writing.

3. Now you are ready for _____ education.

4. Any news outlet would be fortunate to _____ you.

5. We've been happy to be _____ you in your high school years.

MISSION 3: Proofread your client's essay for admission to journalism school. Highlight any grammar errors.

As an aspiring journalist, my desire too be accepted into journalism school is fueled by a love for storytelling, a curiosity about the world, and a commitment to truthful reporting.

From a young age, I've being fascinated by word's ability to inform inspire, and create change. Journalism will allow me to use my love for writing as a force for good. I want to give voice to the voiceless, shed light on untold stories, and hold those in power accountable. Journalism is not just a job for me, it's a hire calling.

Journalism school offers myself the chance to improve my writing and develop as a reporter. I'm excited to learn from experienced journalists and professors. My classes and activities will provide me with the tools you need to excel in this rapidly changing field.

I'm also looking forward to learning besides diverse peers who share my enthusiasm for reporting. Promises to be intellectually stimulating and personally fulfilling. The American journalism school will challenge me and refine my skills. With training, I believe I can right to inform, inspire, and foster understanding.

In conclusion, I am eager to put fourth my best efforts as a student. Being accepted into journalism school would not only be a great honor. But also a major step towards realizing my dream.

MISSION 4: Message Client Z some encouragement about her essay. Proofread your message.

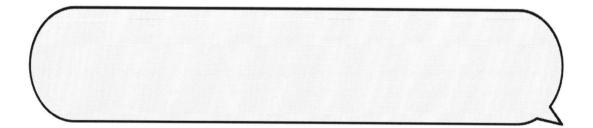

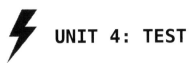 # UNIT 4: TEST

Review the Fast Facts and grammar graphic sections of Operations 25-32. Then ask your trainer for the Unit 4 test. Record your score below.

Number correct out of 50_____ x 2 = _____ %

If you didn't score as well as you hoped, complete some review exercises you can find at FunToLearnBooks.com/FastGrammar2.

SOLUTIONS

⚡ OPERATION 1: PARTS OF SPEECH REVIEW

Part of Speech	Sentence
TRANSITIVE VERB	The book Calvin & Hobbes <u>gave</u> me the giggles as a kid.
PREPOSITION	All the books <u>on</u> the shelf are mine.
CONJUNCTION	The books' pages have many highlights <u>and</u> annotations.
INTERJECTION	<u>My goodness</u>, how I enjoy reviewing those yellow notes.
ADVERB	<u>Later</u> I'll show you some of my favorites.

MISSION 1: Highlight 15 errors.

1. Wow. Its exciting to be a client for fast grammar. [Wow! It's exciting to be a client for Fast Grammar.]
2. I was asked to send messages but wasn't sure where to. [unnecessary preposition]
3. So giving it a try. [incomplete sentence following the conjunction]
4. This is a amazing idea. [should be **an**]
5. I hope you can correct my grammar easy. [should be **easily**]
6. My friend and I run a Social media business.
7. This Fall we want to add more clients.
8. I'm the Founder of our company.
9. I have a sister in your program, and we have two Beagles.
10. Both beagle's nickname is couch potato. [should be **beagles'**]

MISSION 2: Add the correct word to the blank.

1. We're happy to <u>hear</u> that you're excited!
2. <u>Here</u> at Fast Grammar, we want happy clients.
3. Our trainees get to know grammar and their clients before we turn them <u>loose</u>.
4. With our technology's superiority over autocorrection, you can't <u>lose</u>.
5. But if you have any issues, we want to <u>hear</u> about them.

MISSION 3: Review the graphic your client submitted. Highlight the correction and part of speech.

fast Grammar

Hear are 5 reasons to try Fast Grammar's human autocorrection service:

1. **Saves time.** Fixing <u>autocorrections'</u> mistakes takes time you don't have.
2. **Accuracy.** Fast <u>grammar</u> is correct 99.5% of the time.
3. **Saves embarrassment.** Ugh! Human autocorrectors know what you mean to say. <u>You</u> won't look foolish or insult someone.
4. **Easy to use.** Text <u>your</u> autocorrector once a week and <u>soon</u> grammar mistakes will be replaced in real time.
5. **You have nothing to <u>loose</u>!** Fast Grammar <u>offers</u> a free trial. If it doesn't work <u>for</u> you, cancel <u>any</u> time.

Hear **Here**	transitive verb intransitive verb **neither**
autocorrections' **autocorrection's**	possessive pronoun proper noun **neither**
grammar **Grammar**	**proper noun** adjective neither
You Your	**personal pronoun** possessive pronoun neither
your you	personal pronoun **possessive pronoun** neither
soon sooner	**adverb** adjective neither
loose lose	transitive verb preposition **neither**
offers offer's	**transitive verb** intransitive verb neither
for but	**preposition** conjunction neither
any many	interjection **adjective** neither

⚡ OPERATION 2: CONCRETE VS. ABSTRACT NOUNS

MISSION 1: Highlight 11 ABSTRACT NOUNS in the messages.

1. Hello! I want to tell you more about my hopes for this program.
2. Writing is happiness for me. But I need to improve my grammar and spelling.
3. My dream is to become an investigative journalist.
4. I need an excellent English score on my college test to make that happen.
5. I also need to improve my grammar skills.
6. But writing truth is most important to me.
7. I have made progress in my writing, but I still have things to learn.
8. Besides my education, friendship is a priority.
9. In college, I hope to meet other journalism students who write with bravery.
10. I believe that integrity creates beauty. I hope you agree.

MISSION 2: Add the correct homophone from the graphics to each blank. **Also choose from *here/hear*.**

1. <u>Here</u> at Fast Grammar, we can help you improve your grammar and your English score.
2. We don't want you to <u>lose</u> respect because of mistakes.
3. Autocorrection's rules are too <u>loose</u> for journalists like you.
4. It can mistake a word with an incorrect <u>capital</u> letter for a name.
5. Fast Grammar will be there as you write from your hometown or from the steps of the <u>capitol</u>.

MISSION 3: Highlight the needed changes in the column on the right.

A recent <u>gallup poll</u> found that 60% of
₁
Americans have little to no trust in the news. Instead,

a majority of those polled

say they see political <u>bias</u> that poses
₂
a threat to democracy. Integrity is the key to

restoring trust in the news.

    Here's how <u>the community times</u>
₃
will demonstrate that integrity. We will

adopt clear <u>policy's</u> for the following:
₄
- fact-checking
- printing corrections
- declaring funding sources

We want to restore our <u>reader's</u> trust by
₅
getting the facts right, printing articles from

diverse political perspectives, and employing

multiple ombudsmen who critique our work.

1. A. NO CHANGE
   B. Gallup Poll
   C. Gallup poll
   D. Gallup polls

2. A. NO CHANGE
   B. Bias
   C. bias's
   D. biasis

3. A. NO CHANGE
   B. The Community Times
   C. The Community Time's
   D. the Community times

4. A. NO CHANGE
   B. Policy's
   C. Policies
   D. policies

5. A. NO CHANGE
   B. readers'
   C. Reader's
   D. Readers'

With consistency in demonstrated

integrity, we hope to restore your trust in
6

the media.

6. Which is a concrete example of integrity in the article?
   A. There are NONE
   B. bias
   C. declaring funding sources
   D. democracy

133

OPERATION 3: INTERROGATIVE & DEMONSTRATIVE PRONOUNS

Rule Number	Example sentence
1a	**Who** took my pen?
3c	**This here** is my pen. - incorrect
2	**Whatever** did you think you were doing?
3a	**This** is the pen I've had since 7th grade.
3b	**Those** are my shoes.

MISSION 1: Highlight the 10 INTERROGATIVE AND DEMONSTRATIVE PRONOUNS he used.

1. Thanks for your help last week. Now what is the next step?
2. This is the part of the program I don't understand.
3. Like who will take over for my autocorrector when he or she finishes Fast Grammar?
4. What is the privacy policy for my communication?
5. If my sister and I both have requests, whose is handled first?
6. That is what I need to know to feel comfortable.
7. And when does the program end?
8. Which of the grammar errors do you see most?
9. Whatever will I do if Fast Grammar cancels their program?
10. These are a few more questions I have for you.

MISSION 2: Review the homophone graphics below. Add the correct homophone from the graphics or use *lose/loose*.

1. When your autocorrector finishes training, you will not <u>lose</u> our services.
2. To reassure you, we are not <u>loose</u> with your personal information.
3. We have a strict privacy policy agreed to <u>by</u> your autocorrector.
4. When you <u>buy</u> access to the Fast Grammar program, you aren't competing for help.
5. One thing your autocorrector will look for is proper nouns without <u>capital</u> letters.

MISSION 3: Rewrite the copy correctly on the blank poster on the right.

It's time to hire a professional.

WHAT IF YOU HAD TIME TO FOCUS ON YOUR MOST PROFITABLE ACTIVITIES?

You will when you hire MARKETING MENSA'S team.

WHEN YOU BUY OUR SERVICES, YOU BUY MORE TIME.

**This is your chance.
Contact us today!**

⚡ OPERATION 4: NOUNS & PRONOUNS USED AS ADJECTIVES

MISSION 1: Highlight the 11 ADJECTIVAL NOUNS she used.

1. You won't believe what happened to my dad's sports car.
2. It was stolen from the lot by our apartment complex.
3. Two teens who are too young to drive broke the window and started it without a key.
4. The police officer who took the report told us we were unlikely to get the car back.
5. But my mother posted a picture of the car on social media and someone had seen it!
6. We got the car and took it to an auto repair shop.
7. We heard from our insurance company agent that these thefts were on the rise.
8. My father was given a courtesy car to drive.
9. Then he got a shocking phone call.
10. His repaired sports car had been stolen again from the auto shop!

MISSION 2: Add the correct word from the graphics or use *here/hear* or *lose/loose.*
1. We are so sorry to <u>hear</u> about your father's car.
2. To <u>lose</u> a car to theft once is bad, but twice?
3. Your father probably wasn't holding his <u>breath</u> on getting the car back the first time.
4. We hope he will not have to <u>buy</u> a new car.
5. He has our sympathy <u>here</u> at Fast Grammar and well wishes on getting the car back again.

MISSION 3: Client Z wants you to review part of her article about auto theft. Please highlight the corrections to be made on the right and answer the question that follows.

The Forest Park Police Department reports an 85% increase in

<u>Auto thefts</u>. The majority of the increase has been blamed on a design
1

flaw in some car models. My father's sports car was stolen twice!

1. A. NO CHANGE
B. auto theft's
C. auto Thefts
D. auto thefts

Viral videos show kids how to start these <u>cars models,</u> using only a
2

USB cord. Many of the thieves are too young for a <u>driver license,</u>
3

yet they are committing a crime that would be a felony in many states.

2. A. NO CHANGE
B. car models
C. cars' models
D. Car models

3. A. NO CHANGE
B. driver's license
C. Driver License
D. Driver's license

The auto manufacturers most affected by these thefts have been

working to develop <u>software updates</u> that will prevent the USB bypass
4

from working. However, some car owners aren't ready to <u>breath</u> with
5

relief. Instead, they are expressing their frustration with the situation,

questioning why the automakers did not anticipate this security

vulnerability and take steps to address it earlier. Some have even filed

lawsuits against the companies.

4. A. NO CHANGE
B. Software update
C. Software updates
D. software's update

5. A. NO CHANGE
B. breathe
C. breathing
D. breaths

In the meantime, authorities are urging <u>car owners</u> to <u>by</u>
6   7

6. A. NO CHANGE
B. car's owners

steering wheel locks, use GPS tracking systems, and park in well-lit

areas. My father will be purchasing another car model.

How many of the underlined words/phrases above include adjectival nouns?

C. cars' owners
D. Car owners

7. A. NO CHANGE
   B. buy
   C. bye
   D. own

8. A. NONE
   B. 2
   C. 4
   D. 6

OPERATION 5: VERB CONJUGATION

to eat

Subject	Tense	Progressive	Standard
1st Person S	Present	I am eating.	I eat.
1st Person P	Past	We were eating.	We ate.
2nd Person	Future	You will be eating.	You will eat.
3rd Person S	Present Perfect	She has been eating.*	She has eaten.
3rd Person S	Past Perfect	He had been eating.*	He had eaten.
3rd Person P	Future Perfect	They will have been eating.	They will have eaten.

to give

Subject	Tense	Progressive	Standard
1st Person S	Present	I am giving.	I give.
1st Person P	Past	We were giving.	We gave.
2nd Person	Future	You will be giving.	You will give.
3rd Person S	Present Perfect	She has been giving.*	She has given.
3rd Person S	Past Perfect	He had been giving.*	He had given.
3rd Person P	Future Perfect	They will have been giving.	They have given.

*She/He/It are correct.

MISSION 1: We asked Client X to text you about his week. Highlight the 4 sentences in PERFECT OR PERFECT PROGRESSIVE TENSE.

1. You saved me with the edits to my poster. Thank you!
2. I have been making a lot of grammar mistakes.
3. And I had reviewed the poster before sending.
4. But I obviously missed some errors.
5. Now I'm wondering about lost business due to my grammar.
6. But I've heard my grandma say, "No use crying over spilled milk."
7. And I've heard my dad say, "Onward and upward."
8. So I guess I will try to learn from you going forward.
9. I hope to make more money because I'm your client.
10. But you don't guarantee that, right?

MISSION 2: Review the grammar graphics below. We will respond to your client with the text messages that follow. Add the correct word from the graphics or use *by/buy*.

1. Fast Grammar <u>lets</u> you do what you do best.
2. You can focus on your business when you <u>buy</u> our service.
3. Potential grammar errors can leave you <u>breath</u>less with anxiety.
4. We want you to <u>breathe</u> a sigh of relief now that we're on the job.
5. As for a guarantee, <u>let's</u> just say we want to support you any way we can.

MISSION 3: Review the product landing page your client created for a customer. Review the <u>underlined</u> words and choose the change or answer for each on the right.

Virtual Pickleball <u>will be</u> the fast-paced, futuristic game that keeps players on their toes with a simulated ball of light that bounces off the walls and ceiling. It's the spaced-out version of pickleball you can play in your living room.

How to Play
Playing Virtual Pickleball is easy! Use your electronic "racquet" to return the ball ... or play solo against the game console. Scorekeeping is automatic. The first one to 11 wins! But the game is so much fun, you can't <u>loose</u>. <u>Simply turn on the game console, grab your racquet, and "hit" the ball.</u> The game is designed with beginners in mind, so you can start playing right away!

What's Included
Virtual Pickleball includes everything you need. It comes with 2 racquets, so you can start playing with a friend or family member immediately. The game console is compact and easy to set up.

Benefits of Playing Virtual Pong
People who play Virtual Pickleball <u>have saw</u> many benefits. It's a great way to get some exercise while having fun. You can play with friends or family members, and it's suitable for all ages. It's also a great way to improve your hand-eye coordination and reflexes. And you can stay home to play this popular game. No more waiting for a court!

Buy Now
Don't wait to get your hands on this exciting new game. Virtual Pickleball <u>let's</u> you play with friends and family indoors. And it will be the best gift you <u>have ever gave</u>. Order now and start playing today!

---

1. will be
a. NO CHANGE
b. is
c. was

2. loose
a. NO CHANGE
b. lose
c. loss

3. The sentence is in:
a. 1st person
b. 2nd person
c. 3rd person

4. have saw
a. NO CHANGE
b. saw
c. have seen
d. seen

5. let's
a. NO CHANGE
b. let us
c. lets

6. have ever gave
a. NO CHANGE
b. have gave
c. have ever given
d. ever given

⚡ OPERATION 6: PREPOSITIONS

Past Tense Verb	Sentence About Sleep
lay (lie)	I lay down to sleep an hour ago, but I'm still awake.
laid (lay)	I laid my favorite blanket on the bed first.
(sat) sit	Earlier, my dog sat on it and then fell asleep.
set (set)	I set my clothes out before I got into bed.
rose (rise)	Yesterday I rose still feeling tired.
raised (raise)	I raised the shade right away, hoping it would wake me.

MISSION 1: Highlight the 3 INCORRECT VERBS she used in the messages.

1. Ever since my dad's car was stolen, I've had trouble sleeping.
2. I laid down at the usual time.
3. But I keep thinking I hear something.
4. I raise up and look out the window.
5. When I see nothing, I set down and try to relax.
6. I get back into bed, but I'm wired.
7. My dad set up a video security system.
8. The system raised my hopes that I'd be able to sleep.
9. But I still can't lay my head on the pillow and sleep through the night.
10. I make sure I've set my alarm and laid out my clothes, but I'm late rising.

MISSION 2: Add the correct homophone from the graphics or from *breath/breathe*.

1. You <u>have</u> our sympathy for your insomnia.
2. A good night's sleep <u>lets</u> you do your best work.
3. Have you tried taking a deep <u>breath</u> before you lie down at night?
4. Have you tried a warm cup <u>of</u> cocoa before bed?
5. <u>Let's</u> hope one of these strategies reduces your anxiety.

MISSION 3: Highlight necessary corrections to underlined words as indicated in the right column.

Sleep plays a vital role in the physical and mental well-being of teenagers. I've learned that the hard way since my dad's <u>sports' car</u> was stolen. However, many kids my age find it difficult to get enough sleep due to academic demands, social activities, and screen time. These are some tips I'll be following to get enough z's.	**1. sports' car** a. NO CHANGE b. sport's car c. sports car
Establish a Consistent Sleep Schedule: We should aim to go to bed and wake up at the same time each day, even on weekends. That seems crazy, but doctors say that having a regular time to <u>lay</u> down will work with our circadian rhythm and not against it.	**2. lay** a. NO CHANGE b. lie c. laid
Create a Sleep-Friendly Environment: Our sleep environment should be relaxing. This means keeping the bedroom cool, dark, and quiet. Minimizing the use of electronic devices, such as smartphones and laptops, before bedtime can also improve sleep quality. I have a bad habit of using screens before I sleep and as soon as I <u>rise</u>.	**3. rise** a. NO CHANGE b. raise c. risen
Practice Relaxation Techniques: Deep breathing exercises and reading a print book can promote a calm and peaceful state of mind, making it easier to fall	**4. sit** a. NO CHANGE

asleep. I have also found it helpful to journal. I write out my worries and an action to take for each. I <u>sit</u> the journal aside and feel less stressed.	b. sat **c. set**
Limit Stimulants and Large Meals: When you've had trouble sleeping, caffeine could <u>of</u> been the problem. We should avoid caffeinated drinks, particularly in the afternoon and evening, as they can interfere with falling asleep. Many experts also recommend eating small amounts within three hours of bedtime, so Indigestion is less likely to keep us up.	**5. of** a. NO CHANGE b. had **c. have**
Getting enough sleep is required for teens to function at their best. <u>Lets</u> see if establishing a consistent sleep schedule, creating a sleep-friendly environment, practicing relaxation techniques, and limiting caffeine and large meals will help us get the sleep we need.	**6. Lets** a. NO CHANGE **b. Let's** c. Lets'

⚡ OPERATION 7: ADJECTIVE OR ADVERB

easy	I had an easy time making friends when I was younger.
slow	I made friends the slow way.
real	My neighbor is a real friend.
calm	He has a calm personality.
bad	He never has a bad attitude.
well	He is great even when he doesn't feel well.

MISSION 1: Highlight the 4 ADJECTIVES or ADVERBS he used incorrectly in the messages.

1. My friend and business partner and I aren't getting along well.
2. He doesn't feel good about our focus.
3. He says he can create graphics easy.
4. But landing pages like the Virtual Pickleball one are really hard for him.
5. I used a calm voice, but he was real upset.
6. He wants to build the business more slow than I do.
7. He says we can limit our focus and still make money easily.
8. I want to get lots of jobs until we really know our specialty.
9. I feel badly that we aren't getting along.
10. But for now we see our business differently.

MISSION 2: Add the correct word from the graphics or from *let's/lets*.

1. We know you didn't ask for our <u>advice</u> on your business.
2. We could <u>have</u> asked for your permission to offer it first.
3. But if one business partner <u>lets</u> the other have his way,
4. the amount <u>of</u> conflict will decrease significantly.
5. In the meantime, you could ask a business coach to <u>advise</u> you.

MISSION 3: Highlight necessary corrections to underlined words as indicated in the right column.

I hope you are doing well. I have been listening to your business podcast and would love your advise on an important decision for the social media business my friend and I run. My friend and I disagree on whether to specialize <u>immediately</u> or provide lots of services to get more sales. While I understand the benefits of niching down, I'm not sure if it's the right approach since we're just getting started. On one hand, specializing in a specific niche within social media (like videos) could allow us to become experts <u>quick</u>. We could also stand out from our competitors. However, I am concerned about limiting our growth potential by narrowing our focus too much.	**1. advise** a. NO CHANGE b. advice c. Advise **2. immediately** a. NO CHANGE b. immediate c. quick **3. quick** a. NO CHANGE b. quickly

On the other hand, I feel <u>good</u> about trying to serve larger audience. It seems we could make more money. However, I know there is more competition if we try to do it all. If you would <u>of</u> started a social media business at my age, would you have specialized in one area or no? What are the pros and cons? And do you have any tips for running a business when the partners don't agree? I feel <u>badly</u> for taking your time, but I greatly appreciate your recommendations. Best regards,	c. of **4. good** a. NO CHANGE b. well c. badly **5. of** a. NO CHANGE b. had c. have **6. badly** a. NO CHANGE b. bad c. well

⚡ OPERATION 8: EMOTIONAL INTERJECTIONS

MISSION 1: Highlight the 6 INCORRECT COMPARISONS she used in the messages.

1. I am sleeping better and I'm glad.
2. But I'm still most anxious. - *unnecessary*
3. I thought I would feel a lot more better by now.
4. My mom suggested I exercise more.
5. She says exercise has made her feel less stressed.
6. Watching workout videos had her exercising more consistently.
7. She was getting strongest every day. – *should be stronger as it's comparing to previous day*
8. But the girl stopped making videos, so my mom started going to the gym oftener.
9. Now she tries to lift her best heaviest weight each time.
10. I'm thinking of going with her to get more fit and have less anxiety too. – *should be fitter*

MISSION 2: Add the correct homophone from the graphics. Also choose from *have/of*.

1. Did you decide to take your mother's <u>advice</u> about exercise?
2. Exercise doesn't <u>ensure</u> a decrease in anxiety, but it can't hurt!
3. Perhaps your mother would <u>have</u> had more anxiety about the car if she hadn't been exercising?
4. Like her, we would <u>advise</u> you to try exercising more.
5. Just curious. Did the rate to <u>insure</u> your dad's car go up?

MISSION 3: Highlight necessary corrections to underlined words as indicated in the right column.

In a stressful, uncertain world, managing anxiety has become an even <u>more essential</u> skill. I wanted some tips to manage my own worries, so I reached out to some local mental health experts. These were their top strategies.	**1. more essential** a. NO CHANGE b. essentialer c. most essential
First, they recommended a healthy lifestyle. Regular exercise, a balanced diet, and <u>more better</u> sleep can decrease anxiety levels. Physical activity relieves muscle tension and helps us get to sleep. A healthy diet and a regular sleep schedule improve energy and productivity, giving us less to be anxious about.	**2. more better** a. NO CHANGE b. better c. betterer
A second strategy experts mentioned was self-care. This category includes activities like spending <u>less time</u> reading or watching news; having a regular quiet time for meditation, prayer, or relaxation; and dedicating time to hobbies and activities that improve mood.	**3. less time** a. NO CHANGE b.less c. lesser
A third strategy experts mentioned was social support. Talking about worries with trusted friends, family, or support groups decreases anxiety even if we don't get <u>advise</u> for specific problems.	**4. advise** a. NO CHANGE b. advice c. advises
Finally, the experts I consulted recommended seeking professional help when anxiety becomes overwhelming. Therapists and counselors can teach <u>less effective</u> techniques such as cognitive-behavioral therapy (CBT) to address underlying thought patterns and develop effective coping mechanisms.	**5. less effective** a. NO CHANGE b. effective c. most
While anxiety is even <u>more common</u> these days, these expert-recommended strategies offer a path to peace. By incorporating these techniques into our lives, we can regain control and find freedom from worry.	**6. more common** a. NO CHANGE b. commoner c. most common

⚡ OPERATION 9: PARTS OF A SENTENCE REVIEW

Sentence with a compound subject	You and I communicate well.
Sentence with a compound predicate	I work hard to both talk and listen.
Sentence with a compound subject and predicate	You and I communicate and resolve conflicts well.
Negative pronoun used correctly	Nothing can get between us.
Comma separating a statement from the question *do I?*	I have stated my position clearly, haven't I?
An unessential appositive	I had to work out a disagreement with Ashley, my friend since childhood.
A quotation used as a subject	"I'm sorry" is a great way to start resolving conflict.

MISSION 1: Highlight the word(s) in BRACKETS in each message.

1. Didn't go well. I mean the business agreement wasn't signed. [SENTENCE FRAGMENT]
2. My friend said he couldn't hardly believe I was having him sign a legal form. [DOUBLE NEGATIVE]
3. He said "I think I should have my attorney look at this." [WORD THAT SHOULD BE FOLLOWED BY A COMMA]
4. I founded the business and asked him to be my partner. [COMPOUND PREDICATE]
5. Now he, my best friend, is treating me like I'm a con artist. [APPOSITIVE]
6. He can't sue me can he? [WORD THAT SHOULD BE FOLLOWED BY A COMMA]
7. He says we have to consider the ideas, the time and the talent we bring to the business. [WORD TO BE FOLLOWED BY AN OXFORD COMMA]
8. I kept saying, He can't be serious! [WORDS THAT SHOULD BE IN QUOTES]
9. Don't throw our friendship away over this Jack. [word that should be followed by a comma]
10. He and I have been friends forever. I don't know what to do. [COMPOUND SUBJECT]

MISSION 2: Add the correct word from the graphics or *advice/advise* to each blank.

1. We know you want to <u>ensure</u> that you stay friends with Jack.
2. We assume that he used to be your <u>confidant</u>.
3. You would probably seek his <u>advice</u> for situations like this.
4. Our role isn't to <u>advise</u> you on conflict resolution.
5. However, we feel <u>confident</u> that you will work things out.

MISSION 3: Review the email to his business partner that your client submitted. Find each grammar concept indicated to the right of the paragraph and highlight it in the email. Then check the box.

Dear Jack,

Hope you're doing well. This email might seem a bit serious, but I want to talk to you about something important. After thinking it through, I've come to the tough decision that we should end our business partnership.

First off, I want you to know that our friendship means a lot to me. This decision has nothing to do with how I feel about you personally. It's about what's best for Marketing Mensas.

I think it's important for us to sit down and have an open conversation about this. Can we find a time to meet up soon? Maybe we could meet and get frozen yogurt?

Since our friendship is "important," I want to make sure we handle this the right way. Maybe we can ask the business coach, the guy I told you about, to meet with us virtual. I am confidant he can help us reach an agreement.

You and I could also talk to my dad's lawyer. She can tell us the right steps to end a partnership. She's said she would help me "any time." You can't never have too much advice am I right? We can figure out how to divide everything in a fair way.

- ☐ compound subject
- ☐ sentence fragment
- ☐ compound predicate
- ☐ incorrect quote
- ☐ should be adverb
- ☐ appositive
- ☐ wrong spelling
- ☐ comma should follow
- ☐ double negative
- ☐ correlative conjunction

I believe that by both discussing everything openly and working together, we can wrap up our business partnership in a friendly way. Thanks for understanding, and let's find a time to chat soon. Take care,	

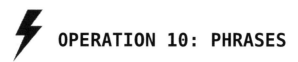 **OPERATION 10: PHRASES**

MISSION 1: Highlight each PHRASE that modifies the underlined word.

1. My anxiety about the car theft has decreased.
2. The tips I wrote about have helped me.
3. Yesterday afternoon I played pickleball.
4. The sport, played with a paddle and a wiffle ball, is easy to learn.
5. A line near the net is called the kitchen.
6. I lost points for stepping into the kitchen.
7. But all of us had fun playing.
8. Later that night I slept well.
9. Exercise, specifically pickleball, is my sedative.
10. This nonathletic, indoorsy writer is actually playing a sport.

MISSION 2: Add the correct word to the blank. Also choose from *ensure/insure*.

1. What piqued your interest in pickleball originally?
2. Does a decrease in anxiety mean you don't peek out your bedroom window at night?
3. Are you confident that you'll continue to sleep well?
4. Are you doing anything else to get into peak physical condition?
5. When you enjoy a sport, you ensure that it will become a habit.

MISSION 3: Client Z wants you to read her article about pickleball. Please highlight the part of speech of each underlined phrase.

In a sporting revolution, pickleball has taken the nation by storm, captivating players of all ages.

This unique paddle sport has become the hottest trend in the athletic world. With its smaller court, specialized paddles, and perforated plastic ball, pickleball offers an exciting and fast-paced experience. Communities across the country are embracing this new phenomenon, witnessing a surge in participation at local community centers, parks, and recreational facilities.

What sets pickleball apart is its accessibility and inclusivity. Players of all backgrounds and athletic abilities can play. It's the perfect game for families, friends, and even retirees seeking a fun and social way to stay active.

The rise of pickleball can be attributed to its simplicity and quick learning curve. The rules are easy to understand, allowing beginners to quickly grasp the fundamentals.

In addition, pickleball offers significant health benefits. Players can have a great time while enhancing their overall well-being.

1. **In a sporting revolution**
   A. noun phrase
   B. adjective phrase
   C. prepositional phrase

2. **This unique paddle**
   A. prepositional phrase
   B. adjective phrase
   C. verb phrase

3. **at local...facilities**
   A. prepositional phrase
   B. adjective phrase
   C. verb phrase

4. **of all backgrounds**
   A. prepositional phrase
   B. noun phrase
   C. both A and B

5. **can be attributed**
   A. prepositional phrase
   B. verb phrase
   C. adjective phrase

6. **health**
   A. adjectival noun
   B. subject
   C. adverb

Experts predict that <u>pickleball's</u> popularity will only continue to soar. So, grab your paddle and start playing!

7. **pickleball's**
A. possessive noun
B. adjective
C. both A and B

⚡ OPERATION 11: ADVANCED CLAUSES

Pickleball, *a paddle sport*, has been increasing in popularity.
People tell us that pickleball, a paddle sport, is increasingly popular in their communities.
Young and old people alike enjoy playing pickleball.
People who are young and old alike enjoy playing pickleball.
New pickleball players can play *surprisingly well*.
After just a few games, new pickleball players can play surprisingly well.

MISSION 1: Highlight 5 SUBORDINATE CLAUSES in the messages.

1. I met my friend to discuss ending our partnership.
2. When I arrived at the smoothie place to meet him, I was shocked.
3. I thought the email that I sent was clear.
4. But my friend took my email as a threat.
5. He brought two people, his dad and his dad's attorney.
6. He said his opinion was whatever the two of them had to say.
7. After I adjusted to the shock, I was mad.
8. I wanted to protect the friendship by having this meeting.
9. But my friend only seemed to care about money.
10. They all threatened to sue me when I walked out the door.

MISSION 2: Add the correct homophone to the blank. Also choose from *confident/confidant*.
1. We are sure the meeting had a terrible <u>effect</u> on you.
2. We hope you won't let it <u>affect</u> you too much going forward.
3. No one gets to the <u>peak</u> of the mountain without going through some valleys.
4. It's disappointing when you get a <u>peek</u> at a darker side of a friend.
5. But we are <u>confident</u> that things will work out.

MISSION 3: Find at least one example of each grammar concept indicated to the right of the paragraph and write the line number(s) in the email where it can be found.

1 Jack, I can't believe you had your dads lawyer, send me a letter, when I 2 was trying to work this out with you! You are apparently agreeing with 3 everything that he says. 4 The letter says I need to "cease and desist." I had to get the definition of 5 that. What do you want me to stop doing exactly? I'm so confused. 6 The letter also says that all business assets are effectively frozen. I had to 7 look that up too! First, what business assets are you talking about? We 8 have used the little bit of money we've made to advertise the business. 9There is no money to freeze! 10 The lawyer says you can sue me for damages. Again, what damages? 11 What money have you lost? I read that you can sue for pain and 12 suffering in a lawsuit. If that's true, then I have a case. I am suffering! 13 I thought we were "friends." We disagreed on the direction for the	<u>1, 4, 6, 10, 11, 17</u> noun clause <u>10,18</u> sentence fragment <u>3, 8, 16</u> adjective clause <u>13</u> incorrect quote <u>1-2, 14</u> adverb clause <u>17</u> wrong spelling <u>14</u> comma should follow <u>1</u> missing apostrophe <u>17</u> should be an adverb <u>1</u> shouldn't have comma after

148

| 14 business. Because we couldn't agree I felt we should end our
15 partnership. I wanted to end it and keep our friendship. But the
16 friendship that we've had for years doesn't seem to be important to you.

17 I can't describe how bad this has effected me. I hope you'll have your
18 lawyer "cease and desist." So we can work this out. | |

⚡ OPERATION 12: INFINITIVE FORMS

to write as an adjective I have many papers to write.
to write in an infinitive phrase I need to write a 5-paragraph essay.
to write as a perfect infinitive I want to have written 500 words before bed.
to write as a progressive infinitive I want to be writing by 10 a.m.
to write as a perfect progressive infinitive I seem to have been writing for only a few minutes, but it's been an hour.

MISSION 1: Write the number(s) for the type of infinitive used in each message in the blank.
1 – noun, 2 – adjective, 3 – adverb, 4 – perfect, 5 – progressive, 6 – perfect progressive

1. I'd like to teach my mom to play pickleball.   ___1___
2. I told her that it's such a fun sport to play.   ___2___
3. She doesn't like to be making mistakes.   ___1, 5___
4. But I told her that she needs to have played first.   ___1, 4___
5. I explained that I play pickleball to relax.   ___3___
6. Now I won't miss my time to play.   ___2___
7. She says she wants to practice alone first.   ___1___
8. But to play is to be practicing.   ___1, 5___
9. She seems to have been making excuses for weeks.   ___2, 6___
10. By next week, I want to have played with her once.   ___1, 4___

MISSION 2: Add the correct homophone to the blank. Also choose from *peak/peek/pique*.

1. So you're <u>already</u> encouraging family to play pickleball? That's great!
2. Have you <u>already</u> played with your brother
3. We are glad that pickleball has had such a positive <u>effect</u> on your anxiety.
4. Perhaps you can <u>pique</u> your mom's interest just by having her watch you play.
5. The <u>effect</u> of modeling your enjoyment is very powerful.

MISSION 3: Highlight the correction that should be made to each underlined portion.

Lately I've been trying to get my mom <u>to be playing pickleball</u> with no success. I've learned that while I cannot force her to change, I can inspire and influence her. If you'd like someone to change, these strategies may help you. **Lead by Example**: The best way <u>to inspire change</u> in others is to live it. By consistently demonstrating positive behavior, we can become a powerful role model who encourages others to follow suit. I keep playing pickleball and telling my mom how much fun I'm having. **Empathy and Understanding:** <u>To have changed</u> someone, we must first understand their perspective and motivations. By actively listening we make it safe for them to trust us. I have expressed understanding when my mom says she isn't athletic.	**1. to be playing pickleball** a. NO CHANGE b. to play pickleball c. to have played pickleball **2. to inspire change** a. NO CHANGE b. to be inspiring change c. to have inspired change **3. To have changed** a. NO CHANGE b. To be changing c. To change

Highlight Benefits: People are more likely to welcome change when they understand the potential benefits it can bring. I have shared with my mom how playing pickleball has decreased my anxiety and increased my energy.

    Support and Encouragement: Providing practical help and encouragement can be the difference in someone's willingness to change. I have told my mom that I will play with her privately and I had expressed my belief in her ability to play.

  Although change is always an individual's choice, we possess the power to influence and inspire transformation in others. I had all ready used some of these strategies, but my mom just asked if I wanted to show her how to play pickleball! When we lead by example, practice empathy, highlight the benefits, and provide support, we make it easier for others to do better.

4. had expressed
a. NO CHANGE
b. had been expressing
c. have expressed

5. all ready
a. NO CHANGE
b. already
c. completely

6. to do better
a. NO CHANGE
b. to improve
c. to change

⚡ OPERATION 13: COMMAS

MISSION 1: Highlight 14 words or digits that should be followed by COMMAS in the messages.

1. I heard back from Jack my business partner.
2. He said he was just diagnosed with diabetes so that explains why he was freaking out.
3. He saw Michael Jacobs MD for a physical and got the shocking news.
4. He said "I couldn't believe it!"
5. Anyway he apologized.
6. He said he isn't going to sue me for $10000 now.
7. He said "You'll forgive me won't you?"
8. I will forgive him but can I trust him?
9. I have so many questions about his diagnosis our friendship and the business.
10. Does having diabetes a disease that causes high blood sugar explain his behavior?

MISSION 2: Add the correct word to the blank. Also choose from *affect/effect*.

1. We have to <u>compliment</u> you on how you're handling the conflict with your friend.
2. Have you <u>already</u> told him you need to meet and talk
3. We do think it's possible for diabetes to <u>affect</u> your friend's behavior.
4. But do you think he is a good <u>complement</u> to your skills in business?
5. You should be honest about the conflict's <u>effect</u> on you.

MISSION 3: Review your client's essay on diabetes for health class. Highlight the correction needed.

My friend was recently diagnosed with diabetes. I wanted to understand its <u>affect on him</u> so I did some research. The first thing I learned is that diabetes <u>been increasing</u> among teenagers. It can affect them physically, emotionally, and socially.

<u>First diabetes</u> affects teens physically. Without checking blood sugars, eating at the right times, and taking insulin, serious damage to the body can occur. Hyperglycemia <u>or high blood sugar</u> can make it difficult to concentrate, while low blood sugar can cause confusion and shakiness.

Next, there are emotional effects of diabetes. Fear of low- or high-blood-sugar episodes can be distracting. Management of the condition can take time away from studying. Feeling different may lead to self-consciousness.

Finally, there are social effects of diabetes. Diabetic teens may limit eating and exercising with friends, or they may ignore their condition <u>to hopefully fit</u> in. Isolation and uncontrolled blood sugars can make the emotional effects worse.

I <u>had all ready</u> learned that diabetes is a blood-sugar disease. Now I know what a challenge it will be for my friend to manage it physically, emotionally, and socially. I want to <u>complement him, when</u> he takes care of himself. I want him to be around for a long time.

1. affect on him
a. NO CHANGE
b. affect on him,
c. effect on him,

2. been increasing
a. NO CHANGE
b. has been increasing
c. has been increased

3. First diabetes
a. NO CHANGE
b. First of all diabetes
c. First, diabetes

4. or high blood sugar
a. NO CHANGE
b. , or high blood sugar
c. , or high blood sugar,

5. to hopefully fit
a. NO CHANGE
b. to fit
c. to hopeful fit

6. had all ready
a. NO CHANGE
b. have all ready
c. had already

	6. complement him, when
	a. NO CHANGE
	b. complement him when
	c. compliment him when

⚡ OPERATION 14: DASHES & PARENTHESES

MISSION 1: Add 13 DASHES and PARENTHESES and highlight them where they belong in the messages.

1. Well, my mom played pickleball (the sport she wasn't interested in!) with me. *em dashes are also correct*
2. It took her playing from 3:00–4:00 to get comfortable on the court.
3. There were three shots she loved—lobs, smashes, and dinks.
4. After a warmup, she was trying to hit overhead smashes from the kitchen.
5. I had to explain (multiple times!) that kitchen shots can only be hit off the bounce. *em dashes are also correct*
6. I also had to repeatedly explain the scoring (0–0–2) to start the game.
7. The other thing I had to remind her (50 60 times, I think) was not to hit a volley on the return of serve. *em dashes are also correct*
8. So, here's the funny thing—she's playing more than I am now!
9. Some of the neighbors were playing and invited her to play in their league (2–3 days a week).
10. She's been playing so much that the J is worn off her paddle (it reads —OOLA now).

MISSION 2: Add the correct homophone to the blank. Also choose from *all ready/already*.

1. We <u>knew</u> your mom would enjoy pickleball if she tried it!
2. And now she <u>already</u> has a league to play in.
3. What a <u>compliment</u> to be invited to play.
4. You introduced her to a <u>new</u> sport.
5. Will she be <u>all ready</u> to play doubles with you when you have time?

MISSION 3: Add any needed punctuation and highlight it. Also highlight any misspelled words. *Optional commas aren't included.*

KNEW PICKLEBALL LEAGUE FOR TEENS

New Century Park
12345 State Street
Canton, Michigan

THURSDAY NIGHTS, 6:30–8:00

All skill levels (beginner to advanced) are welcome. After a brief lesson we'll match you with players to compliment your level of experience.

If you're ready for a little competition (you are, aren't you?), join the league.

Please bring an outdoor ball, pickleball paddle, and bottled water (and maybe a friend too)! You'll be already to have fun. Note that adults (aka parents) have a league meeting Mondays and Wednesdays.

No need to RSVP. Just join us next Thursday night, September 18th.

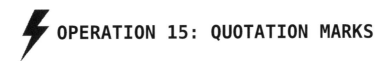

OPERATION 15: QUOTATION MARKS

MISSION 1: Add 10 sets of QUOTATION MARKS where needed and highlight them.

1. Jack said he is feeling better since his diabetes diagnosis.
2. He said he's been singing James Brown's song "I Feel Good" a lot.
3. Even though he's feeling better, he said, "I'm not sure about continuing in the business."
4. He said, "My dad told me, 'Keep the main thing the main thing.' But I don't know if our business is the main thing?"
5. I said I thought "main thing" means his health.
6. He admitted that he isn't really "feeling good."
7. "It's been a lot harder to deal with than I thought," he said.
8. I said, "Don't worry about the business right now. My song for you is 'You've Got a Friend in Me.'"
9. He said he appreciated my patience with him.
10. But I did remind him that the word "Mensas" in our business name means there is more than one genius at work.

MISSION 2: Add the correct homophone to the blank. Also choose from *compliment/complement*.

1. It sounds like Jack is managing well with a <u>new</u> diagnosis.
2. We have to <u>compliment</u> on you on how you are treating him.
3. You're the one who <u>oversees </u>the business with no partner now.
4. Have you considered hiring some <u>overseas</u> help? *new is also correct*
5. We hired a virtual assistant and we never <u>knew</u> it could be so beneficial!

MISSION 3: Highlight 14 errors. Note: Each comma and set of quotation marks is considered one error.

We are seeking a highly skilled oversees "virtual assistant" to remotely join our team. As a virtual assistant in a complimentary role, you will complete a variety of tasks in our social media business—creating graphics, scheduling posts, and updating our website.

The ideally candidate will have had excellent communication skills, strong attention to detail, and the ability to work independently with minimal supervision. Candidates should all ready be fluent in English. Prior experience with Canva, a graphic design program, is a plus. Experience working with social media is preferred.

This is a remote position, requiring flexibility to have been working across different time zones. If you are motivated, hard-working, and eager to contribute to our team, we would love to hear from you. To insure that you are considered for the position, please send us your resumé with "Virtual Assistant" in the subject line.

⚡OPERATION 16: COMBINING SHORT SENTENCES

MISSION 1: Highlight 3 sets of consecutive messages that could easily be COMBINED INTO ONE SENTENCE.

1. I was so excited about the pickleball league.
2. I had talked to lots of friends about it.
3. I was sure they were coming.
4. But no one showed up!
5. My friend Becca said she had too much homework.
6. To my surprise, I got no response to my text messages from anyone else that night.
7. My friend Lily later admitted she was binge watching a show.
8. She's unreliable.
9. So I guess I'm not playing pickleball now.
10. My mom suggested I play in her league, but ugh.

MISSION 2: Add the correct homophone to the blank. Also choose from *knew/new*.

1. We are sorry that <u>fewer</u> people showed up than you hoped.
2. It is a <u>new</u> league, however.
3. As a company that <u>oversees</u> group activities, we have experienced this initial disappointment.
4. It seems that you <u>knew</u> not to expect your friend Lily to show up.
5. We're sorry that you seem <u>less</u> excited about pickleball now.

MISSION 3: Review your client's essay on using time-out. Then set a timer and follow the directions in the box to the right.

I have been playing pickleball. I have been loving it. I thought starting a pickleball league for my friends was a fantastic idea. Several people said they'd heard of it and wanted to try it. I was sure that the league would be a success, but it was not.

I have been playing pickleball and loving it.

I would not have been upset if a small group had joined the league. Instead, no one showed up to the first night. At first, I thought it was a bad night. And I should have sent a reminder. But then I realized that there was another reason: busyness.

At first, I thought it was a bad night and I should have sent a reminder.

Teens my age feel too busy. Between schoolwork, extracurricular activities, part-time jobs, and social obligations, the demands on their time seem never-ending. This busyness often leads to stress and lack of sleep. It leads to limited time for fun activities like pickleball.

This busyness often leads to stress, lack of sleep, and limited time for fun activities like pickleball.

While a certain level of activity is good for us, we need to find a balance. We have to use time management. We have to set realistic goals. And we need to get help making decisions. Then we might have time to join a pickleball league.

We have to use time management, set realistic goals, and get help making decisions.

OPERATION 17: ADVANCED PARTS OF A SENTENCE

For each sentence part indicated, write an example sentence about the things that keep you busy.

irregular plural noun	*Playing pickleball with people keeps me busy.*
linking verb	*I am busy with math homework.*
indirect object	*My mother gives me chores to do.*
compound object pronoun	*She assigns tasks to my brother and me.*

MISSION 1: Highlight the SENTENCE PART indicated in brackets.

1. I haven't been able to find a VA who checks all the boxes. [plural noun]
2. One seemed talented but stopped responding to messages. [linking verb]
3. I asked every work candidate to give me a sample graphic. [indirect object]
4. Jack and I reviewed them. [subject pronoun]
5. Some candidates gave us the impression that their English wasn't good. [object pronoun]
6. Misspellings don't look professional, as you know. [linking verb]
7. We didn't discourage these candidates by mentioning the spelling. [direct object]
8. We may not be able to hire them, however. [object pronoun]
9. We will ask candidates to send additional samples to Jack and me. [object pronoun]
10. We may end up having to interview a whole new group of people. [irregular plural]

MISSION 2: Add the correct homophone to the blank. Also choose from *oversees/overseas*.

1. It sounds like your quest to find help has been <u>quite</u> difficult.
2. We imagine that <u>fewer</u> international candidates are proficient in English.
3. Will you continue to consider <u>overseas</u> candidates?
4. Has Jack been <u>quiet</u> as he adjusts to his diagnosis?
5. We hope there has been <u>less</u> tension between the two of you.

MISSION 3: Review your client's essay on how to hire a VA. Highlight the corrections to be made on the right.

<u>My friend and me</u> want to hire a virtual assistant. I've learned that it's
₁
important to follow these steps to find the right candidate. First, define the

specific tasks and <u>responsibilitys</u> you want your virtual assistant to handle.
₂
Then, thoroughly research and vet potential candidates. You don't want to

roll a <u>dice</u> to choose someone! Consider their experience, skills, and
₃
communication style. Conduct interviews or trials to assess their

compatibility with your working style. Does the applicant <u>seem quite</u>? Do
₄
they complete the assignment quickly and correctly? We asked several

applicants to create graphics for <u>Jack and I</u>. Check references and reviews
₅
to make sure they are reliable and trustworthy. Clearly communicate

expectations, deadlines, and payment terms upfront. Finally, establish a

system for ongoing communication and feedback. That's what we plan to

do when we find the right virtual assistant <u>for us</u>.
₆

1. A. NO CHANGE
   B. Me and my friend
   C. My friend and I
   D. Him and I
2. A. NO CHANGE
   B. responsibilities
   C. responsibility's
   D. responsibilite's
3. A. NO CHANGE
   B. dies
   C. die
   D. die's
4. A. NO CHANGE
   B. seem quietly
   C. seems quite
   D. seem quiet
5. A. NO CHANGE
   B. Jack and me
   C. we two
   D. him and I
6. A. NO CHANGE
   B. for we
   C. for he and me
   D. for Jack and I

⚡ OPERATION 18: PROBLEMATIC SUBJECT/ VERB AGREEMENT

MISSION 1: Highlight 6 INCORRECT VERB FORMS in the messages.

1. My driver's license or job applications is on my mind right now.
2. The test on laws and punishments was easy.
3. But the number of things the driving evaluator will check worry me.
4. I could get one of those evaluators who marks everything wrong.
5. Many a student have failed the test the first time.
6. The written test and the driving eval is the last step before I get my license.
7. The Driving Association of the Americas is the sponsor of the driver's ed course I took.
8. The number of hours of driving experience required before testing are 40 in my state.
9. There are only two places to go for the driving test.
10. Once I pass, I hope the Bears hire me as a ticket agent!

MISSION 2: Add the correct homophone to the blank. Also choose from *less/fewer*.

1. If you pass your driving test, you'll <u>formally </u>be a driver!
2. That's exciting and <u>quite</u> a milestone.
3. We won't say who, but one of us took the driver's test no <u>fewer</u> than four times before passing.
4. If that makes you nervous, we'll be <u>quiet</u>.
5. One of our staff members was <u>formerly</u> a ticket agent for a sports team.

MISSION 3: Review your client's injury report for her life skills class. Then set a timer and follow the directions in the box to the right.

The debate surrounding teen <u>drivers revolve</u> around the question of ₁ what age young drivers like me should be allowed to get a license. The argument for raising the driving age for teen <u>drivers is</u> that it would reduce ₂ accidents involving inexperienced drivers. Brain development <u>or maturity</u> ₃ <u>play</u> a crucial role in responsible driving. On the other hand, many <u>an</u> <u>opponent argue</u> that the driving age should remain as it has been <u>formally</u>. ₄ ₅ A license, they say, offers freedom and independence to teens and prepares them for adulthood. They emphasize the need for good driver education. The driving age debate is <u>one of those issues that are</u> likely to ₆ continue, while I hope to get my license soon!	1. A. NO CHANGE
	   B. driver's revolve
	   C. drivers revolves
	   D. driver revolves
	
	2. A. NO CHANGE
	   B. drivers are
	   C. driver's is
	   D. drivers' are
	
	3. A. NO CHANGE
	   B. or maturity plays
	   C. and maturity play
	   D. either B or C
	
	4. A. NO CHANGE
	   B. a opponent argues
	   C. a opponent argue
	   D. an opponent argues
	
	5. A. NO CHANGE
	   B. formerly
	   C. formal
	   D. former
	
	6. A. NO CHANGE
	   B. one of those...is
	   C. one of this...are
	   D. one of these...is

OPERATION 19: VERB TENSE

MISSION 1: Highlight 4 INCORRECT REFLEXIVE/INTENSIVE PRONOUNS.

1. I haven't had any luck finding a VA by myself.
2. I gave myself a deadline of two weeks and that has passed.
3. Jack and myself started this business ourselves.
4. I thought I would always have him alongside myself.
5. I told Jack I was having trouble, and he said he would try to find help himself.
6. While he does that, I'm taking it upon myself to find another solution.
7. I'm testing artificial intelligence for tasks you don't have to do oneself.
8. AI can accomplish many tasks itself that I was doing.
9. For example, I am asking it to find business owners who aren't doing social media theirselves.
10. AI can even write introduction emails to them by itself!

MISSION 2: Add the correct word to the blank. Also choose from *quite/quiet*.

1. Using AI in your business could increase your profits.
2. You don't have to be a prophet to think that AI will be managing many of our tasks in the future.
3. Things that formerly took us hours AI can do in minutes.
4. Have you formally given up on your search for a VA then?
5. Has Jack gotten back to you, or has he continued to be quiet?

MISSION 3: Review your client's meme and post. Highlight 11 errors. The word MYSELF should be highlighted in the meme. Note: *AI* below should be in parentheses.

My business partner and me have had no luck finding a VA. We want to save ourselves time without giving up prophets. Then I read that artificial Intelligence AI can complete some tasks formally performed by virtual assistants (VAs). As an example, AI made this meme for my partner and myself. The only thing I had to do myself was enter the text! AI assistants for various social media is able to determine the best time to post and then schedule those posts. AI chatbots can answer client questions and respond to messages for yourself, too, reducing the amount of time you have to spend online. A AI assistant can save oneself time and money. However, human VAs' creativity, empathy, and sense of humor are difficult for AI to copy. That's why business owners like us may want to do theirselves a favor and have a VA as well as an AI assistant.

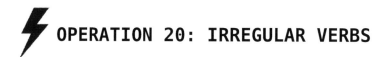

OPERATION 20: IRREGULAR VERBS

MISSION 1: Highlight 4 INDEFINITE PRONOUNS/ADJECTIVES THAT DON'T AGREE WITH THEIR VERB.

1. I took my driver's test where everyone fails.
2. At least, few of my friends has passed.
3. Neither of my older cousins was able to pass their test there.
4. If most are failing their test, shouldn't they get a new evaluator?
5. Any driver feel nervous when being rated on their driving.
6. Some of the drivers who failed are afraid to go back!
7. In that case, something tell me it's not the drivers' fault.
8. I came to a fork in the road where the evaluator said, "Either are fine."
9. I went the wrong direction down a one-way street as many have.
10. But no one is happier than I am to report that I passed the test anyway!

MISSION 2: Add the correct word to the blank. Also choose from *formerly/formally*.

1. Congratulations! Now you are ready to proceed with your job application.
2. We're surprised that going the wrong way is what preceded you passing your test.
3. In this case, your friends and family weren't good prophets.
4. You are formally a licensed driver.
5. Now you can profit from having a job.

MISSION 3: Review your client's article on the benefits of teens having jobs. Highlight 10 errors.

I just got my driver's license and I'm ready to apply for my first job. There are less teens working than in past decades, but the rate is increasing. Some of the reasons for the lower rate is the economy, the requirement for volunteer hours for scholarships, and the internships that are unpaid and not included in employment statistics.

Experts agree that working too many hours while going to school can proceed negative affects of teen employment such as lower grades. However, there are numerous benefits to be gained. First, a job provides an opportunity for teens like me to gain valuable experience. A few of the things we can learn is responsibility, time management, teamwork, and problem-solving. Jobs also teach financial literacy, as we learn the value of money and how to budget. In addition, employment fosters independence and self-confidence. Some jobs helps us explore possible career paths and discover our interests. Finally, employment can give us a strong work ethic, discipline, and a sense of accomplishment. Overall, teen employment offers invaluable life lessons. It can set ourselves up for future success personally and professionally.

Most teens works in food service. I am hoping to get a job as a ticket agent. Anyone who have an "in" with the Bears should contact myself.

⚡OPERATION 21: PRONOUNS, SPECIAL CASES

The two students, her and Grace, attended the meeting. – incorrect
The two students, she and Grace, attended the meeting.

The director gave the two students, she and Grace, free tickets to the concert. – incorrect
The director gave the two students, her and Grace, free tickets to the concert.

We wanted to attend the concert more than them [wanted to]. – incorrect
We wanted to attend the concert more than they.

MISSION 1: Highlight 6 INCORRECT PRONOUNS in these informal messages.

1. Well, the two partners, Jack and me, are back in business!
2. I told him what I learned about AI.
3. I explained that it could be better than him!
4. That was my joking at his expense. [correct, but formal]
5. I said I needed a new partner, a VA, AI, or he.
6. I had him watching some videos on what AI can do.
7. He gave himself and myself a deadline for making a decision.
8. He knew I was less interested in hiring a VA than he.
9. After his review of AI possibilities, he is ready to get back to work.
10. The three of us, AI, Jack, and myself, are a team.

MISSION 2: Add the correct word to the blank. Also choose from *profit/prophet*.

1. That's great news. Now you can <u>proceed</u> with your business plans. [*profit* is also correct]
2. You're going to <u>adopt</u> AI technology rather than hire a VA,
3. but will you need to <u>adapt</u> it so it works for your business?
4. Will any kind of training need to <u>precede</u> your use of AI?
5. We hope this partnership with AI will increase your <u>profit</u>s.

MISSION 3: Your client asked AI to write copy for their marketing business. We asked AI to add 11 grammar errors for you to find. Please highlight them.

Introducing Marketing Mensas, the innovative social media marketing business powered by the brilliance of two teens, Jack and I. With their fresh perspective, digital savvy, and passion for social media, we are redefining the marketing game.

Marketing Mensa's combines cutting-edge strategies with a deep understanding of social media platforms to boost your prophets like never before. Harnessing our youthful creativity and tech-savviness, Jack and myself develop ingenious content strategies, captivating campaigns, and engaging visuals that resonate with your target audience.

Marketing Mensas specializes in skyrocketing brand visibility, driving organic growth, and maximizing conversions. We not only adapt the latest trends, we adopt them to make them work in your business. With regards to our competitors, we will deliver better results than them—guaranteed!

With Marketing Mensas, you gain the advantage of young minds with a pulse on the digital world, including how to take advantage of AI. Our fresh ideas and out-of-the-box thinking will make your brand as competitive as it.

Ready to precede and level up your social media presence? Let Marketing Mensas, Jack and me, take your business to new heights! Contact us today for a consultation and get ready to witness the power of youthful brilliance.

OPERATION 22: AMBIGUOUS PRONOUN REFERENCE

Answers will vary.

My mother and sister disagreed about her curfew, and she looked upset.
My mother and sister disagreed about her curfew, and my sister looked upset.
My mother takes good care of her golf clubs. It is her favorite sport.
Golf is my mother's favorite sport, so she takes good care of her golf clubs.
Put the telescope to your eye and adjust it until it's clear.
Put the telescope to your eye and adjust the eyepiece until the view is clear.

MISSION 1: Highlight 8-9 PRONOUNS WITH AMBIGUOUS OR INCORRECT REFERENCES.

1. As you know, I got my license last week. It has been fantastic!
2. My dad and brother congratulated me, but I think he's jealous.
3. He told me that I would have my own car to drive. – *"My dad" is assumed, but not clear.*
4. But that we would have to split the insurance deductible.
5. I think they can be very expensive! – *"insurance deductible" is singular.*
6. I may need to get a job to pay for it. – *it may be highlighted or not because "insurance deductible" wasn't referenced in the last message.*
7. I asked my dad if my brother would have to pay half my share when he gets a license. – *"he" isn't ambiguous because we know "dad" already has a license.*
8. My dad said that he may pay half my share unless we get another car for him.
9. My brother thinks he should get a new car now.
10. Then my brother can have his old car. – *"his" isn't ambiguous because we know "brother" doesn't yet have a car.*

MISSION 2: Add the correct word to the blank. Also choose from *proceed/precede*.

1. It's so exciting that you <u>passed</u> your driving test.
2. Many families <u>adopt</u> rules for car usage that are
3. identical to their <u>past</u> experience as teens.
4. Other families <u>adapt</u> the rules because cars and insurance are so expensive now.
5. Let us know how you decide to <u>proceed</u>.

MISSION 3: Review your client's list of pros and cons of teens paying for their own vehicle. Follow the directions in the right column.

I just got my driver's license, and my father has asked that I pay half the insurance deductible before driving his car. That got me wondering about the pros and cons of teens paying for their own vehicles. In the (passed), most young people paid for their own cars. I know he did! There <u>is</u> three benefits of a teen contributing to the purchase of their own vehicle: financial responsibility, ownership pride, and work ethic.	Highlight 3 pronouns with ambiguous antecedents (except *they* referring to *teens*).

First, contributing <u>instill</u> a sense of financial responsibility and independence. They learn the value of money, budgeting, and the importance of making informed financial decisions.

Second, by purchasing their own vehicle, teens <u>develops</u> a sense of ownership pride and accountability. It is more likely to take better care of the vehicle, ensuring regular maintenance and responsible driving habits.

Third, paying for a vehicle <u>require</u> teens to work, save, and develop a strong work ethic. They learn the importance of setting goals, working hard, and delaying gratification, which can translate into other aspects of their lives.

But there are also some drawbacks of teens paying for their own vehicle: financial strain, insurance costs, and distractions.

First, purchasing a vehicle is a significant financial commitment, and it may place a burden on teens like me who are still studying or working part-time. They can divert funds from other essential needs, such as education or savings.

Second, insurance premiums for teenage drivers are typically high due to their lack of experience. Teens may struggle to afford these premiums on top of other expenses, making car ownership financially challenging.

Finally, owning a vehicle can introduce distractions and shift priorities for teens. They may become more focused on their car and social activities, which can precede declines in academic performance and other responsibilities.

Ultimately, assessing individual circumstances, finances, and parents' guidance will (proceed) the decision to have a teen pay for a vehicle or not. My dad thinks having me pay half the insurance deductible is a good compromise.

<u>Underline</u> 4 incorrect verbs.

(Circle) 2 incorrectly spelled words.

OPERATION 23: COMMONLY MISSPELLED WORDS

MISSION 1: Highlight 18 misspelled words in the messages.

1. I truely think AI can make us more successfull.
2. The peice of copy I sent you is the jist of what it can help us acheive.
3. Basicly, AI automates the writing process, so we feel like Neandarthalls in comparison!
4. The knowlege it draws from is immediatly and publically available.
5. The new millenium of progress does not dissappoint!
6. Is good writing skill realy even necessarry now?
7. The time savings of using AI to write is iresistible!
8. No, AI can't copy the idiosyncrasies of an individual's style.
9. And goverment and politicians are worried about propoganda.
10. But I think we're on the threshhold of a great new era of progress.

MISSION 2: Add the correct homophone to the blank. Also choose from *adapt/adopt*.

1. Even with AI, it's important to know how to <u>write</u> well.
2. It sounds like you think AI has <u>passed</u> your test for a valuable tool.
3. Many people are <u>adopt</u>ing AI as a business tool.
4. You may be <u>right</u> that this is the beginning of a new era.
5. But we believe that we will have to <u>adapt</u> AI's writing to make it more personal and effective.

MISSION 3: Review your client's AI-generated copy for a foreign-language learning company. Highlight 15 spelling errors we added.

Discover a World of Languages — Embrace the Multilingual Journey!
Are you tired of feeling limited when traveling or working across borders? Are you curious about different cultures and want to communicate effortlessly with people from various parts of the globe? Look no further. Our Foreign Language Course is here to help you achieve your language learning goals!

Embark on a Glamorus Adventure:
Step into a world of excitement as you begin your journey into the rich and diverse world of languages. We accommodate learners of all levels, from beginners to advanced, ensuring you find the perfect fit for your language learning needs.

Unlock New Opportunities Across the Globe:
Speaking a foreign language opens countless doors in business, government, and other sectors. Imagine impressing colleages and potential clients with your fluency in Portugese or navigating the Caribean with ease.

Beyond the Basics:
Our course goes beyond the basics. Delve deep into the peculiarities and idiosyncrisies of each language, gaining a deeper understanding of their culture and enviroment.

The Gist of Communication:
Master the essentials of communication — the vocabulary, grammer, and pronunciation — that will make you confident and irresistible in any conversation. No longer will you feel embarassed by language barriers.

Knowledge That Stands the Test of Time:
With our experienced instructors and proven teaching methods, you'll be well prepared for any forign language dilemma that may arise. You'll notice a significant improvement in your language skills as you progress through the course.

Surprizes Await You:
As you learn, you'll discover fascinating similarities and differences across languages, and occasionally, bazarre idioms that will keep you intrigued. With the global landscape changing rapidly, the ability to right and speak foreign languages is more necessary than ever. Be prepared for unforseen circumstances and grab opportunities wherever they may arise.

Join Our Multicultural Committee:
Our language-learning community is like a supportive commitee, encouraging you every step of the way. Forge connections with fellow learners from different backgrounds, fostering an environment of camaraderie and learning. Don't let language barriers hold you back; take the first step in your foreign language journey today! Remember, tomorrow's success is built on today's effort. Enrol now and embrace the extraordinary world of languages!

⚡ OPERATION 24: WRITING NUMBERS

MISSION 1: Highlight 7 NUMBERS THAT ARE WRITTEN INCORRECTLY.

1. $500 is the insurance deductible I have to pay. [should not be at the beginning of the sentence]
2. That works out to me having to work forty hours to pay for insurance.
3. That's if I get a job making $15 an hour.
4. If I worked ten hours a week and 50 weeks a year,
5. that means I'd be spending .07 (7%) of my $7500 income on insurance.
6. That feels like seven million to me!
7. I'm not sure I want to work in fast food, measuring out ten cups of sugar for lemonade like my friend does.
8. I also have to pay for gas, which is $3 a gallon—
9. a lot more than the $1.19 my dad paid as a teen.
10. I'm thinking of trying to get proofreading jobs that pay three dollars a page.

MISSION 2: Add the correct homophone to the blank. Also choose from *past/passed*.

1. So, you'd rather <u>pore</u> over other people's papers
2. than <u>pour</u> sugar into a batch of lemonade?
3. Proofreading others' work will help you <u>write</u> better.
4. It's amazing how inexpensive things were in the <u>past</u>.
5. We didn't check your math, so we'll assume you're <u>right</u> about the percentage of your income you'll pay for insurance.

MISSION 3: Review the flyer Client Y made for Client Z. Highlight 14 number and spelling errors.

Are you tired of submitting documents with embarassing typos and grammer mistakes? Do you want your writing to leave a lasting impression on your readers? Look no further. My proofreading service is here to make your content shine!

Why Choose Me?
Attention to Detail: I pour over your content to insure that any errors disapear.

Wide Range of Content: I proofread academic papers, busyness reports, essays, and creative writing.

Fast Turnaround: I understand deadlines. Rest assured, you'll receive 1 to ten-page documents within forty-eight hours and longer documents within a week.

Confidentiality Guaranteed: Your documents are safe with me. I have submitted interesting stories to local papers, but I respect your privacy.

Affordable Rates: Quality proofreading doesn't have to break the bank. My rate is only three $ per page!

How It Works:
1. Email your document to me.
2. Recieve a quote based on the number of pages in your document.
3. Once payment is confirmed with a $.03 service fee per page, I get to work.
4. Your polished document will be sent back to you immediatly.

Let Your Words Make an Impact:

Students - Impress your professors with flawless assignments and boost your grades.

Professionals – Your writing will give you the appearence of authority.

Authors - Ensure your manuscript is ready for publication.

Righters - Let your creativity pore out while I take care of the details.

Contact me to discuss your project today!

⚡OPERATION 25: ADVANCED GRAMMAR & WRITING REVIEW

Concept #	Example Sentence
1, 3	Skiing is a fun sport, they love going as often as possible.
1, 2, 6	There are lots of things I'm bringing on the ski trip: goggles, helmet, gloves, coat, snow pants.
4, 5	At the thrift store, I found a blue man's hat, new ski gloves, and I found a ski mask.

MISSION 1: Highlight the CONCEPT INDICATED IN PARENTHESES for each message.

1. Writing with AI is much faster. [GERUND]
2. You enter a request; you get the results. [WHERE A SEMICOLON SHOULD BE]
3. I don't know how it researches and writes so quickly; it's truly amazing. [WHERE A SEMICOLON SHOULD BE]
4. After using it many times, it's proven to be reliable. [MISPLACED MODIFIER CLAUSE]
5. I've used it to write social media posts, email, and I've used it to write video descriptions. [THE PART THAT ISN'T PARALLEL]
6. But the fact of the matter is, it's not perfect. [UNNECESSARY WORDS]
7. Some things I've noticed: [WHERE A COLON SHOULD BE]
8. -using the same style of writing for every request [PARTICIPLE]
9. -repeated ideas throughout the writing [PARTICIPLES]
10. -its writing is not really new or interesting [WORDS THAT COULD BE REPLACED WITH ONE WORD] *could be replaced with creative or unique*

MISSION 2: Add the correct word to the blank. Also choose from *write/right*.

1. As you go <u>forth</u>, how will you use AI?
2. We can see how AI would make it faster to <u>write</u>.
3. Was there a <u>fourth</u> thing that you noticed about AI?
4. Do you have to <u>pore</u> over AI's writing, looking for mistakes?
5. It seems <u>right</u> that AI wouldn't write as creatively as you would.

MISSION 3: The client asked AI to write about its use in high school writing. We've added some errors. Highlight changes that should be made.

Using AI for high school writing assignments, <u>it can</u> learn a lot. AI-powered writing assistants can provide real-time <u>feedback: on</u> grammar, spelling, and <u>on sentence structure.</u> <u>With this feedback</u>, students improve their writing skills and self-editing abilities. Moreover, AI can assist in generating topic ideas, organizing content, and <u>source citations</u>, fostering critical thinking and research skills. It offers personalized learning opportunities, catering to individual student needs and <u>pacing. However,</u> it's essential to strike a balance, ensuring students still actively engage in the writing process and maintain their creativity. Teachers play a crucial role in guiding students on effectively utilizing AI tools while emphasizing the importance of originality and understanding the subject matter deeply.

1. it can
a. NO CHANGE
b. they can
c. students can
2. feedback: on
a. NO CHANGE
b. feedback on;
c. feedback on
3. on sentence structure
a. NO CHANGE
b. sentence structure
c. on structure
4. With this feedback,
a. NO CHANGE
b. delete
c. With student feedback,
d. With student feedback;
5. source citations
a. NO CHANGE
b. citing sources
c. sources
6. pacing. However,
a. NO CHANGE
b. pacing, however,
c. pacing: However

OPERATION 26: ACTIVE VS. PASSIVE VOICE

The most books per capita are published in Britain.
Britain publishes the most books per capita.

Amazon self-publishers were paid half a billion dollars last year.
Amazon paid self-publishers half a billion dollars last year

On average, more than 10 hours per week is spent reading by people in India.
People in India spend more than 10 hours per week reading on average.

MISSION 1: Highlight 6 messages in PASSIVE VOICE.

1. I received some responses from several people to my proofreading ad.
2. The first person wanted same-day service.
3. I didn't know that when I took the job.
4. I was told last minute!
5. After that, my terms of service were revised.
6. But then I had another problem.
7. The next client's paper was written so poorly
8. that I didn't know where to begin!
9. Papers that have been edited are what I need.
10. If I could get proofreading work from editors, that would be great!

MISSION 2: Add the correct homophone to the blank. Also choose from *pour/pore*.

1. We have <u>seen</u> some poorly edited papers before, too.
2. You want to see that writers have put <u>forth</u> some effort.
3. Are you proofreading nonfiction, or have you worked on any novel <u>scene</u>s?
4. Aspiring novelists <u>pour</u> their heart and soul into the story.
5. But they also have to <u>pore</u> over their writing in the editing process

MISSION 3: Your client submitted one of her own client's romance-novel pages for your review. Highlight the best description for each underlined section.

In the quaint little town of Sweetville, <u>where love was rumored</u> to
            1
 	
sprinkle like magic dust, stood two souls <u>destined to collide</u>. Amelia, a
            2
 	
spirited florist with a heart as tender as the roses she tended, found
 	
herself swept off her feet by the <u>dashing newcomer, Gabriel</u>. With his
 	
mysterious past and captivating eyes that seemed to hold secrets, <u>it</u>
 	
was like a breath of fresh air in Amelia's world.
 	
   As fate wove its enchanting web, their paths intertwined, and sparks
 	
flew amidst moonlit <u>seens</u>. With every soft touch and whispered word,
 	
their hearts danced to an enchanting rhythm, igniting a love that
 	
bloomed brighter than any bouquet Amelia ever crafted. In Sweetville's
 	
embrace, their love story unfolded, a sweet symphony of passion, hope,
 	
and the promise of a forever they <u>could of</u> only dreamed.
	1. **where love was rumored**
	  A. active voice
	  B. passive voice
	  C. undetermined voice
	2. **destined to collide**
	  A. active voice
	  B. passive voice
	  C. undetermined voice
	3. **dashing…Gabriel**
	  A. passive agent
	  B. subject
	  D. ambiguous reference
	4. **it**
	  A. ambiguous reference
	  B. should be Gabriel
	  C. both A & B
	5. **seens**
	  A. NO CHANGE
	  B. scenes
	  C. scene's
	6. **could of**
	  A. NO CHANGE
	  B. could have
	  C. couldn't have

⚡ OPERATION 27: CONSISTENT SUBJECT/VERB FORMS

Students should proofread their papers, so you can be sure you won't lose points.
Students should proofread their papers, so they can be sure they won't lose points.
Students should proofread their papers to avoid losing points.

She edited her paper, but no errors were found.
She edited her paper but found no errors.

The proofreader reviews the paper carefully and highlighted numerous errors.
The proofreader reviewed the paper carefully and highlighted numerous errors.

MISSION 1: Highlight 5 messages that include UNNECESSARY SHIFTS IN SUBJECT OR VERB.

1. I have been researching our business prospects and it's surprising.
2. AI is taking over and was the number one choice for companies' advertising.
3. Yes, we are being paid now, but will we be paid in the future? [necessary shift]
4. Why should anyone pay when AI can do it for free?
5. I haven't told Jack yet, but the statistics had me worried.
6. More and more businesses are using AI for marketing.
7. Courses on how to use AI for marketing are big sellers.
8. Clients are looking for help, and these courses are being sold to them.
9. It seems like a very different business, but print-on-demand is an option for us.
10. Print-on-demand is excellent passive income, and AI made it happen.

MISSION 2: Add the correct homophone to the blank. Also choose from *forth/fourth*.

1. It's wise of you to <u>appraise</u> the value of your services in light of AI.
2. We have also <u>seen</u> a lot of marketing AI courses.
3. An internet search of marketing services lists AI in the first through the <u>fourth</u> result.
4. Business changed when AI arrived on the <u>scene</u>.
5. When will you <u>apprise</u> your business partner of your research?

MISSION 3: Review the email your client wants to send to his business partner about print-on-demand business. Highlight changes that should be made.

Hey, Jack. I've been thinking about our business, and I <u>had wanted to</u> <u>appraise</u> you of my thoughts. <u>Business is being changed by AI.</u> We <u>have seen</u> the benefits of it. But I am concerned about the future. Why will a company pay us when AI is free? I listened to a podcast, and the benefits of a print-on-demand (POD) business <u>were explained</u>. POD businesses produce custom shirts, bags, and <u>produce custom gifts.</u> POD businesses <u>reduce the need for a large upfront investment in inventory, and operational costs are reduced.</u> The flexibility of POD enables quick adaptation to market trends. And AI can help us with every step of the business—from deciding what to sell to designing graphics. I'll send you a link to the podcast. Let me know your thoughts after you've listened.	**1. had wanted to appraise** a. NO CHANGE b. had wanted to apprise c. want to apprise **2. Business is...AI** a. NO CHANGE b. AI is changing business c. Business is changing AI **3. have seen** a. NO CHANGE b. had seen c. have scene **4. were explained** a. NO CHANGE b. delete c. rewrite sentence

	5. produce custom gifts
	a. NO CHANGE
	b. produce gifts
	c. gifts
	6. reduce the need…
	a. NO CHANGE
	b. reduce operational costs and the need for…
	c. reduces the need for…

⚡ OPERATION 28: GRAMMATICAL MOOD

Mood Number	Example Sentence
5	If I were a millionaire, I'd buy a yacht.
4	When we see the movie, we should get some popcorn.
3	My mother worries about kids who ride bikes without helmets.
2	Grab me a pencil, please.
1	When will you have enough money?
5	The teacher desires that students be heard.
3	There are more than 3,000 billionaires in the world.
1	Are you going to the game with us?
4	If my friend decides not to go, then I wouldn't go.
5	The coach suggested that the player seek a batting coach.

MISSION 1: Highlight 3 INCORRECT VERBS FOR THE SUBJUNCTIVE MOOD.

1. I told my romance-novel client what I thought of her book.
2. That was a big mistake!
3. She said if she'd wanted my opinion of the story, she would have asked.
4. She obviously wishes she was a best-selling novelist.
5. But she is just getting started.
6. She needs more than just proofreading, as you've seen.
7. I recommended that she finds a good editor.
8. She said her mom loves it and that's good enough for her.
9. Her next step is to find a literary agent.
10. If I was an agent, I would give her book a hard pass!

MISSION 2: Add the correct homophone to the blank. Also choose from *seen/scene*.

1. At least you tried to <u>rein</u> in your client's expectations.
2. Her mother is not the best person to <u>appraise</u> her writing.
3. We are sure you were kind when you <u>apprise</u>d her of the need for editing.
4. We are also sure agents have <u>seen</u> a lot of poorly written novels.
5. One of them is sure to <u>rain</u> on her parade, as they say.

MISSION 3: Review the email your client is sending to the romance novelist. Highlight 8 sentences that have the WRONG VERB FORM FOR SUBJUNCTIVE MOOD, HAVE AN UNNECESSARY SHIFT IN SUBJECT OR VERB FORM, or are WRITTEN IN PASSIVE VOICE. <u>Underline</u> 3 incorrectly written words.

Subject: Honest Insights for Your Writing Journey

I hope you are not upset about the writing feedback I gave you. My desire is that my clients are happy with my work.

But I also want my clients to be realistic. You said your dream is to be a full-time romance novelist. I think it's wise to <u>reign</u> in your expectations.

The romance genre is popular with more than $one billion in sales, but you're in a highly competitive market. Succeeding will require exceptional storytelling. The market is saturated, making it difficult for you to gain a following. And over 99% of manuscripts are rejected by publishers.

I've already mentioned the benefits of professional editing. But you should also consider writing in different genres. Of course, the more you write, the more you'll improve. Once you have an excellent book, it wouldn't hurt to hire a social-media marketer like my brother. He can help you build a following that can lead to book sales. Let me know if you want his number.

If I was to guess, I don't see you succeeding as a romance novelist. But that doesn't mean you couldn't write nonfiction. Have you considered writing articles for the local paper? Perhaps you could write book reviews?

If you still desire to write, it is a good idea to remember the obstacles successful authors have faced. The journey must be pursued with dedication, despite its demands and uncertainties.

172

I know you didn't want me to appraise your content, but I want to be honest. I also know you want to put your best work fourth, or you wouldn't have asked me to proofread for you. I wish I was a writing fairy and could make your dream happen for you. But because I'm not, I hope this honest email is the next best thing.

All the best,

⚡ OPERATION 29: COMBINING SENTENCES

Answers will vary.

The movie had a lot of violence.
I found it hard to watch.
The movie had a lot of violence that was hard to watch.

I was looking forward to the movie.
I can't recommend it.
Although I was looking forward to the movie, I can't recommend it.

Can viewers stomach the blood and gore?
That is the deciding factor for seeing the film.
Whether viewers can stomach the blood and gore is the deciding factor for seeing the film.

The movie was playing in multiple theaters.
The movie was playing at multiple show times.
The movie was playing in multiple theaters and multiple show times.

The audience was screaming in fear.
They still seemed to be enjoying themselves.
Screaming in fear, the audience still seemed to be enjoying themselves.

This movie is selling a record number of tickets.
It is a film in the horror genre.
The movie, a film in the horror genre, is selling a record number of tickets.

MISSION 1: Highlight 3 SETS OF ADJACENT MESSAGES THAT COULD BE COMBINED WITH CLAUSES OR PHRASES.

1. After waiting, I haven't heard from Jack about my POD business idea.
2. It's been three days!
3. I don't even know if he listened to the podcast I sent him about POD business.
4. I had my dad listen to it, and he was impressed.
5. Should I start the business without him?
6. I don't know.
7. My dad did say I could have Shiny Object Syndrome.
8. That's the habit of pursuing the latest, exciting thing instead of staying focused.
9. There is a reason to continue with social-media marketing.
10. My sister says she can refer her proofreading clients to me, so that's something to consider.

MISSION 2: Add the correct homophone to the blank. Also choose from *appraise/apprise*.

1. Is there anything <u>besides</u> Jack's lack of response that has you reconsidering a POD business?
2. We are sure you would like to have him <u>beside</u> you in a new business venture.
3. Did your father's mention of Shiny Object Syndrome <u>rein</u> in your enthusiasm?
4. Be sure to <u>apprise</u> us what Jack says about your business idea.
5. Have you <u>appraise</u>d the likelihood of your sister sending you paying clients?

MISSION 3: Review the email your client sent to his business partner. Highlight any ADJACENT SENTENCES THAT COULD BE COMBINED USING CLAUSES OR PHRASES. <u>Underline</u> any INCORRECT WORDS.

Hey, Jack.

I haven't heard back from you about the podcast. That podcast talks about POD business. I'm sure you've been busy. Although I was eager to hear from you, it may be for the best that you haven't responded.

174

I've been thinking about our goals and skill sets. I realized that I wasn't seeing all the possibilities. At first I wondered if I had Shiny Object Syndrome. That's the habit of shifting focus to something new and exciting. It will come as no surprise to you that I suffer from that syndrome. This time, however, I don't think that I should just forget it and move on.

We are a marketing business. We help business owners sell their products and services. But we have also struggled to find clients. What if we start a POD business and use our marketing skills to drive sales? That way we have real numbers to show Marketing Mensa clients! Of course, we would enjoy extra revenue <u>beside</u>.

<u>My idea is to run both businesses</u>. <u>Let me know what you think of that</u>. It would require putting <u>fourth</u> our best efforts. Do you have time to <u>pore</u> yourself into business right now?

I look forward to hearing from you.

⚡ OPERATION 30: SENTENCE VARIETY

MISSION 1: Highlight THE SENTENCE STARTER THAT WOULD ADD VARIETY TO THE MESSAGES.

1. The romance novelist was angry and unappreciative and said she won't need my help again.
2. The woman, an aspiring novelist, doesn't know how to take constructive criticism.
3. She said harshly that she didn't need advice from a high school student.
4. She needs an editor to get published.
5. I don't regret what I wrote despite her response.
6. She is frustrated with herself and taking it out on me.
7. She hasn't written a best-selling romance whether she knows it or not.
8. I am tired and annoyed and not sure I want to keep proofreading.
9. I am rethinking it since working with her.
10. I have taken up running to relax.

MISSION 2: Add the correct homophone to the blank. Also choose from *rain/rein/reign*.

1. <u>Besides</u> a bad experience with that client, do you have another reason for not proofreading?
2. We are fans of running here, but one of us had a serious <u>heel</u> injury.
3. He is wearing a boot while the injury <u>heals</u>.
4. We aren't trying to <u>rein</u> in your running ambition.
5. Make sure you buy a good pair of shoes, however, with the right amount of <u>heel</u>-to-toe drop (difference in height from back to front).

MISSION 3: Review your client's article for aspiring marathon runners. Rewrite the sentences that have a line space beneath them, using the sentence starter in brackets.

I have a few essential pieces of advice for you aspiring marathon runners. [prepositional phrase]
For you aspiring marathon runners, I have a few pieces of advice.
First, create a training plan that gradually increases mileage. Be sure to include rest days to prevent overuse injuries.
Incorporate cross-training and strength exercises to build fitness and reduce injury. [participial phrase]
Incorporating cross-training and strength exercises will build fitness and reduce injury.
Proper nutrition and hydration are crucial. [transition word]
Second, proper nutrition and hydration are crucial.
Fuel your body with balanced meals rich in carbohydrates, proteins, and healthy fats. Practice using energy gels or chews during long runs. Hydrate consistently to avoid dehydration. [infinitive phrase]
To avoid dehydration, hydrate consistently.
Third, invest in good running shoes. You are looking for supportive and cushioned shoes. [two adjectives]
Supportive and cushioned shoes are what you are looking for.
Break the shoes in as soon as you buy a pair. [subordinate conjunction]
As soon as you buy a pair of shoes, break them in.
Listen to your body and don't ignore warning signs of injury. Prioritize sleep for optimal recovery and performance.
Mental preparation is the final step. [transition word]
Finally, mentally prepare yourself.
You will cross the finish line triumphantly when you set realistic goals, visualize success, and cultivate a positive mindset. [adverb]
Triumphantly, you will cross the finish line when you set realistic goals, visualize success, and cultivate a positive mindset.

⚡OPERATION 31: TITLE FORMAT

MISSION 1: <u>Underline</u> TITLES or put them in quotation marks as needed. ==Highlight== WORDS THAT SHOULD BE CAPITALIZED IN TITLE CASE.

1. You probably won't believe this, but Jack is starting a band called <u>==bacon bits==</u>.
2. He said he wrote a song called **"I ==made== an ==omelet== out of ==our breakup==."**
3. He already has an album name: <u>riffs and recipes</u>.
4. If it sells well, he'll publish a cookbook called <u>==culinary chemistry== for ==teens==</u>.
5. He should really call his album <u>==shiny object syndrome==</u>.
6. It doesn't look like we'll be writing <u>==how to succeed in online business==</u> any time soon.
7. I think Jack is as good in the kitchen as Mike of <u>the ==brady bunch==</u>.
8. In an episode called **"==the grass== is ==always greener==,"** Mike has several kitchen accidents.
9. I know Jack is a fan of the TV show <u>the ==monkees==</u> and would like to find three more band members.
10. He says he'll use his ==marketing mensas== experience to market his music.

MISSION 2: Add the correct homophone to the blank. Also choose from *beside/besides*.

1. So Jack won't have time for anything <u>besides</u> the band?
2. Then you're back to being a <u>sole</u> proprietor or businessman.
3. At least you haven't put your heart and <u>soul</u> into a POD business.
4. How are you feeling about not having him <u>beside</u> you as your partner?
5. You were able to <u>heal</u> the relationship in the past. We're sure you will again.

MISSION 3: Your client was asked to create an album cover for his friend Jack. ==Highlight== every word that should be capitalized in title case.

==tracks==
1. "==sizzling strings== and ==savory spices=="
2. "==rock== 'n' ==roll risotto=="
3. "==funky frittata=="
4. "==groovy grub=="
5. "==tunes== and ==tacos=="
6. "==i== have the ==bacon blues=="
7. "==melodies with my munchies=="
8. "==jammin' with muffins=="
9. "==chording in chocolate=="
10. "==i made== an ==omelet== out of ==our breakup=="
==riffs== & ==recipes==

⚡ OPERATION 32: PROOFREADING

Write the number for the error in each sentence below.

Error Number	Sentence
6	Kacy and myself are going to the concert together.
9	We are using her dads tickets from work.
5	She of all my friends are the most excited about this band.
1	We're meeting some other friends their.
4	I seen that the band was going to be here and told Kacy we should go.
2	Because of their popularity.
3	The concert sold out immediately, it's amazing we got tickets.
8	I brought enough money to buy a shirt a drink and a snack.
7	The concert is at the family arena.
10	If we want to get home before midnight, you have to leave before the last song.

MISSION 1: Highlight ANY ERRORS in her messages.

1. Big news to share! [fragment]
2. It's not about the marathon, that's still coming up. [comma splice]
3. I had take the college entrance exam, and I just got my scores back. [incorrect verb tense]
4. My science, math, and reading scores were okay.
5. But my English score was outstanding!
6. What's even better is that I already got a letter from the American school of journalism.
7. They want me to apply for admission and a scholarship to!
8. It, of all the journalism schools, are my top choice.
9. You need a great English score to be accepted, and I'm grateful that I got one. [unnecessary subject shift]
10. I want to thank you for the help you've given my brother and I. [incorrect pronoun]

MISSION 2: Add the correct word to the blank. Also choose from *beside/besides*.

1. You are <u>solely</u> responsible for this achievement!
2. You have poured your heart and <u>soul</u> into writing.
3. Now you are ready for <u>higher</u> education.
4. Any news outlet would be fortunate to <u>hire</u> you.
5. We've been happy to be <u>beside</u> you in your high school years.

MISSION 3: Proofread your client's essay for admission to journalism school. Highlight any grammar errors.

My desire too be accepted into journalism school is fueled by a love for storytelling, a curiosity about the world, and a commitment to truthful reporting.

From a young age, I've being fascinated by word's ability to inform, inspire, and create change. Journalism will allow me to use my love for writing as a force for good. I want to give voice to the voiceless, shed light on untold stories, and hold those in power accountable. Journalism is not just a job for me, it's a hire calling.

Journalism school offers myself the chance to improve my writing and develop as a reporter. I'm excited to learn from experienced journalists and professors. My classes and activities will provide me with the tools you need to excel in this rapidly changing field.

I'm also looking forward to learning besides diverse peers who share my enthusiasm for reporting. Promises to be intellectually stimulating and personally fulfilling. The American journalism school will challenge me and refine my skills. With training, I believe I can right to inform, inspire, and foster understanding.

In conclusion, I am eager to put fourth my best efforts as a student. Being accepted into journalism school would not only be a great honor. But also a major step towards realizing my dream.

COURSE COMPLETION

Well done! I have heard good reports on your quick and accurate grammar correction throughout Level 2 operations.

If you plan to take a college entrance exam, take timed practice tests. Review the extra practice materials for English questions you miss at FunToLearnBooks.com/FastGrammar2.

Congratulations on completing Level 2 grammar training!

If you choose not to join our fictional autocorrection team, you can keep your skills sharp by continuing to proofread your own and others' papers.

Did you enjoy this training? Email us a testimonial we can use in recruitment.

Kirk English

Training Director
info@FunToLearnBooks.com

ABOUT THE AUTHOR

Dr. Melanie Wilson was a clinical psychologist working in a Christian practice, a college instructor, freelance writer, and public speaker before she felt called to stay home and educate her children. She is a mother of six and has homeschooled for 25 years. She says it has been her most fulfilling vocation.

Melanie has always been passionate about language arts and used bits and pieces of different curriculum and approaches to teach her children and friends' children. In 2014, she believed she had another calling to write the curriculum she'd always wanted as a homeschooling mom — one that didn't take a lot of time, made concepts simple and memorable, and was enough fun to keep her kids motivated.

Books have been a family business since the beginning. Melanie's husband Mark has been selling library books since graduating from college. Melanie and the kids have frequently pitched in to help at the annual librarians' conference.

When Melanie isn't busy writing or speaking, she loves playing tennis and pickleball with family and friends.

Melanie is also the author of the *Grammar Galaxy* elementary series, *The Organized Homeschool Life*, and *A Year of Living Productively*. Learn more at HomeschoolSanity.com and FunToLearnBooks.com.

Made in the USA
Monee, IL
30 August 2023

41883904R00101